'He's a charm...

'But he's no match...

Alicia lifted her
David is none of your business!'

'How long have you been engaged to him?'
Jean-Marc asked.

'Six months!' she snapped hotly. 'Not that it's
any of your——'

'A beautiful woman like you?' he cut in, eyes
narrowed. 'Is that really the best you could do?'

Dear Reader

As spring leads into summer, many people's thoughts turn to holidays. This is an ideal time to look out for our holiday reading pack featuring four exciting stories—all set in the beautiful British countryside. The Yorkshire moors, Scotland, the Isle of Wight and Cornwall will be the glorious backgrounds to these four wonderfully romantic tales. Let us know what you think of them, and of stories set in the UK in general. Would you like more of them, or do you prefer more exotic climates? Do tell.

The Editor

Sarah Holland was born in Kent and brought up in London. She began writing at eighteen because she loved the warmth and excitement of Mills & Boon. She has travelled the world, living in Hong Kong, the South of France and Holland. She attended a drama school, and was a nightclub singer and a songwriter. She now lives on the Isle of Man. Her hobbies are acting, singing, painting and psychology. She loves buying clothes, noisy dinner parties and being busy.

Recent titles by the same author:

FORBIDDEN PASSION
DESERT DESTINY

LAST OF THE GREAT FRENCH LOVERS

BY

SARAH HOLLAND

MILLS & BOON LIMITED
ETON HOUSE   18-24 PARADISE ROAD
RICHMOND   SURREY   TW9 1SR

First published in Great Britain 1992
by Mills & Boon Limited

© Sarah Holland 1992

Australian copyright 1992
Philippine copyright 1992
This edition 1992

ISBN 0 263 77604 2

Set in Times Roman 11 on 12 pt.
01-9207-48571 C

Made and printed in Great Britain

CHAPTER ONE

THE steel-blue limousine glided along the drive in the sunlight. Heads were turning. A cluster of reporters moved quietly towards the car—polite, but determined to get a photograph. Conversation at the garden party reached an excited buzz, and as the limousine came to a halt everyone held their breath, champagne glasses clutched in still hands, staring across the landscaped garden to watch.

Jean-Marc Brissac, Last of the Great French Lovers, had arrived.

He stepped out of the limousine. His black hair lifted slightly in the warm breeze, his steel-grey eyes heavy-lidded and his sensual mouth a hard, uncompromising line as reporters moved towards him. He strode past them with a cool nod as the flash-bulbs exploded.

Alicia watched, lifting her glossy black head. She couldn't stand his breed of man. Multi-millionaire, tycoon, playboy—he walked with all the arrogance of French money, his blue-grey suit fitting his powerful muscular body to perfection.

As though he sensed her stare, he looked at her, and a second later ran a strong hand through his black hair as his gaze flashed with quick sexual appraisal over her.

Alicia turned away, her face cool. She was aware of her looks. The red silk dress she wore skimmed her slender curves with sensual emphasis, and her high-cheekboned Latin beauty was as dark as it was smouldering. But, inside, Alicia felt contempt for those who dwelt on physical beauty. Achievement was the only thing in life worth living for.

'I can't face him,' Lindy whispered beside her, stumbling away.

Alicia frowned, concern for her young niece filling her large dark eyes. Putting down her drink, Alicia followed her through the open french windows, and into the spacious drawing-room with its pale lemon walls and elegant chandelier.

'Lindy?' Alicia hovered behind her, studying the girl's bent head. 'Is something wrong?'

Lindy caught her breath, turning to stare at Alicia in surprise, tears brimming in her dark eyes. She looked so young, her pale pink dress emphasising her vulnerability. Alicia's heart ached with love.

'Lindy,' she said gently, 'tell me what's wrong.'

Lindy's mouth trembled. 'What's the point? You'd never understand!'

'Wouldn't I?' Alicia said gently. 'I may be ten years older than you, but I can remember only too clearly what it's like to be a teenager.'

'I . . . I shouldn't tell you about it!' Lindy wiped a tear away with a trembling hand, pushed her soft dark hair from her eyes. 'I feel disloyal to him!'

'Who?' Alicia asked at once, concern in her dark eyes.

Lindy bit her lip. Her dark eyes darted to the door. Then they flicked back to Alicia. There was a pause. Then she said huskily, 'Jean-Marc Brissac.'

Alicia's dark eyes widened with surprise. Involuntarily, she looked over her shoulder to see if Brissac was within earshot. How on earth had

Lindy become mixed up with a man as wealthy and powerful as that? This was a very exclusive party. A high-powered fashion event, littered with famous names and fabulously wealthy people. But this was Alicia's world, not Lindy's. Lindy was only here at Alicia's invitation, and she knew her young niece simply did not mix with people like this. Certainly not with French multi-millionaires like Brissac.

'But I wasn't aware you even knew him, Lindy,' she said.

Lindy gave a shaky sigh. 'Well, you remember I went to Paris in May?'

'On an Italian language course, yes.' Alicia nodded, frowning.

'Well, I made friends with Dominique Dusort,' Lindy said in a rush. 'His goddaughter. At the end of the language course, we were both invited to Château Brissac.'

'And Brissac himself was there?' Alicia asked carefully.

'Not at first.' Lindy continued, 'It was just being looked after by the staff. Dominique and I had the place pretty much to ourselves. Then Jean-Marc came...' She said his name with a sigh of adoration, her lips trembling. 'And he had his girlfriend with him.'

His mistress, you mean, Alicia thought grimly.

'Isabelle Janvier,' Lindy said, jealousy clouding her dark eyes at the mention of the famous French film star. 'She was terribly beautiful, and so sophisticated. But they had an argument, and then Isabelle just walked out. The next morning, Dominique fell off her horse. She fractured her skull and had to be kept in hospital for a few days.'

'Leaving you alone with Jean-Marc Brissac,' Alicia said, her mouth tight.

'Yes . . .' Lindy began to flush a delicate shade of pink. 'Oh, Alicia, he said I could stay on at the château for as long as I liked, and I went to bed thinking how lucky I was. But I couldn't sleep, and when I came downstairs at two a.m. I found him still up, too.'

'He made a pass at you,' Alicia said tightly.

'Oh, no, not at first,' Lindy said quickly. 'He'd been drinking, you see. He was sitting alone, listening to Wagner at full volume, and he looked so gorgeous!' Lindy went on, 'His eyes full of pain, and his tie loosened, and a whisky glass in his hand . . . And I knew I could ease that pain, you see. I knew I could help. So I went over to him and perched on the arm of the chair——'

'How were you dressed?' Alicia asked sharply.

'I—well, I was wearing my nightdress.'

Alicia's dark eyes blazed with fury and she struggled not to show it as she said gently, 'Go on.'

'So I perched on the arm of the chair, and he just stared up at me in silence with those hellish eyes. I told him not to feel so awful about Isabelle. I said that I thought he was the most attractive man I'd ever seen, and that if I'd been Isabelle I would have married him on the spot.' She flushed, adding huskily, 'Then I started to stroke his hair, and he started to kiss me . . .'

Did he? Alicia thought, white with rage.

'I slid down on to his lap,' said Lindy in a hushed voice, 'and he suddenly took me by the shoulders and said, "Get back to bed at once!" I was hurt, so I tried to protest, but he snapped suddenly and pushed me off his lap, shouting at me to get out of the room.'

Alicia breathed a little easier. 'And that was all that—— '

'No.' Lindy shook her pretty head. 'The next morning he must have felt awful about it. He told me if it happened again he would have to send me away. I burst into tears, and he obviously felt sorry for me, because he put his arms around me and comforted me, then asked me to have dinner with him that night.'

'And you said yes,' Alicia muttered with a tight smile.

'Well, of course I said yes!' Lindy broke out hotly. 'I was madly in love with him by then! Alicia, you don't know what he's like! Just to watch him, day after day, see him in so many moods—— '

'What happened after you'd had dinner with him?' Alicia broke in.

'Well, that's when it all started.' Lindy's brows rose in surprise. 'We spent a lot of time together over the next few days. We had dinner every night at an expensive restaurant, we rode together after breakfast, we went for long walks across the Brissac land, we held hands, we talked, we kissed...' Pain shone in her eyes. 'We were like lovers, except that in reality, I suppose, we weren't.'

'You suppose?' Alicia asked sharply.

'I know,' Lindy amended quickly. 'I know we weren't lovers. But Alicia, I was so deeply in love with him!'

'And he took advantage of that!'

'No...! He wouldn't do that! I still believe he cared something for me! It's just that...he didn't care enough!'

'How did it all end, Lindy?' Alicia asked gently, feeling wounded for her niece, seeing the pain of rejection in her eyes and in every breath she took.

'Badly. You see, Isabelle Janvier came back to try and make amends with him. Jean-Marc just dropped me and went off with her. I was so hurt and angry that I caused a big scene with him, accusing him of all sorts of things...'

'Which he denied, no doubt!' Alicia said with cold contempt.

'Yes.' Lindy nodded miserably. 'He also told me I must leave at once. He even telephoned my parents to tell them I was coming home. I just flew home like a corpse, thinking, How could he do this to me?'

Ruthless, then, thought Alicia, and knew the type. She had been involved with someone very similar when she was Lindy's age, and she remembered the pain she herself had suffered.

Falling in love with a sophisticated, powerful and sexy older man at the age of seventeen was rather like running towards a long steel spike and impaling yourself on it.

The phrase, 'How could he do this to me?' was only too familiar, and was exactly how Alicia had reacted to the brutal treatment she had received at the hands of a similar man. Tony Ratchet, she thought with remembered anger, and her eyes blazed at the memory of his dark, attractive face.

Pushing strands of dark hair from her niece's face, Alicia said, 'Don't dwell on it too much, baby.

Men like Brissac are all the same. They take what they want, and they're terribly charming while they're doing it, but once you've served your purpose...' her eyes darkened with cold anger '...they always turn ruthless.'

'Yes...' Lindy stared up at her, mouth quivering. 'That's how it felt! As though he'd just stabbed me and thrown me out of the house. He *was* ruthless. And so brutal...'

Alicia's heart twisted in compassion and anger: she felt fiercely protective towards her young niece. Lindy was Susannah's daughter—and Susannah was all the family Alicia had left.

Alicia had not had an easy life. Her parents had been killed in a car crash when she was seventeen, and at the same time she had received her own taste of Jean-Marc Brissac's type of medicine, from Tony.

Of course, her sister Susannah had offered emotional support, but Alicia had always been independent and proud. In recovering from the double shock she received at seventeen she had added another quality to her character: ambition.

Love was for fools, and Alicia was determined never to be a fool again.

'Poor baby,' she said softly, smoothing Lindy's hair.

'Please don't call me that!' Lindy said, prickling and stepping away from her.

Alicia's hand fell to her side, eyes surprised. 'I'm sorry...'

Lindy looked guilty, bending her head. 'It's just that I don't feel like a baby any more, Aunt Alicia. I'm almost eighteen, and I'm in love with the Last of the Great French Lovers!' She lifted her head with a pride that made Alicia wince. 'He may not be in love with me, but I feel the love of a woman towards him, and that *makes* me a woman. Even if he was brutal to me—he still gave me my first taste of love, and I'm proud that it was him.'

Alicia was appalled, and said, 'Lindy, don't make it worse for yourself! You should be filled with contempt for him, not love!'

'Well, if I reacted like that,' Lindy said on a wave of passion, 'I'd end up like you, wouldn't I? Too beautiful to touch, and too cold to marry, because you look after a career instead of love, marriage and children!'

There was a stunned silence. Alicia stared at her niece, hurt beyond belief by her words. Not that she denied the truth in them: she had quite deliberately planned her life to be like that, and wasn't remotely apologetic for it.

'Lindy,' Alicia said slowly, struggling not to feel hurt, 'don't forget I'm engaged to David Balham. I intend to marry him.'

'You're not in love with him, though!' Lindy said fiercely. 'That's obvious to everyone!'

'I love David,' Alicia said, reeling under the impact of Lindy's attack. 'He's kind, sensitive, and lets me live my life the way I need to. We'll be very happy when we marry. We don't need any grand passion to hold us together—we have friendship.'

'But don't you long to fall in love?' Lindy asked hoarsely. 'To lose your head? To feel so much for someone that you can't sleep at night? To feel sick with love, your heart beating too fast all the time, and——'

'No,' Alicia said, horrified at the very idea. 'I'd rather die than lose control of myself like that.'

Lindy's eyes shot past her. She caught her breath, staring over her shoulder at the open french windows.

Frowning, Alicia turned to see who was there, and saw the detestable Jean-Marc Brissac watching her through heavy-lidded steel-grey eyes as he stood in the doorway, very sure of himself, his hands thrust deep into the pockets of his blue-grey Savile Row suit.

A sardonic smile on his hard mouth, he slid his eyes with that arrogant sexual appraisal over her body, making her pulse-rate soar with sudden inexplicable rage.

'Hello, Lindy.' His voice was a dark, smoky drawl of throaty French power. 'Would you introduce me to your friend? I don't believe we have met.' He stepped forward, brows raised. 'Mademoiselle...?'

Alicia deliberately snubbed him, turning to her niece and saying, 'Would you come with me to find David? I think it's time I left.'

'I...' Lindy floundered, staring at the French multi-millionaire. 'I think I should introduce you to Monsieur Brissac.' She stepped forward, blushing furiously, in an agony of calf-love. 'Jean-Marc, this is my aunt—Alicia Holt.'

'*Enchanté*, Mademoiselle Holt,' Jean-Marc drawled, grey eyes narrowed and frowning. 'Forgive me—but *have* we met before?'

'No,' Alicia said icily. 'Come along, Lindy.' She took Lindy's arm in a firm grip, determined not to leave her to the mercy of this ruthless bastard.

Lindy shook her off. 'I must speak to Jean-Marc alone!' she said in a burst of adolescent emotion.

Jean-Marc Brissac frowned, eyes hardening as he studied her, but he did not attempt to stop her, even though he must have known she would only make a fool of herself if she stayed.

Alicia looked at him, hatred flashing from her dark eyes. 'Very well,' she said, moving away from her niece. 'I'll wait for you outside.'

As she walked towards him, Jean-Marc Brissac's grey eyes ran over her with narrowed appraisal, and Alicia felt that inexplicable rage flare deep inside her, looking at him through her dark lashes, her red mouth tight with dislike.

The hot summer sunshine warmed her bare shoulders as she stepped into the gardens. Men slid admiring glances at her as she passed, but she was indifferent to them, her only concern to get Lindy away from the wolf.

She saw David, drinking champagne and eating a salmon sandwich while perched on a wall in his grey suit, enjoying the sunshine and the look of all these expensive, beautiful guests, staring around with a smile, obviously amused by his exclusive surroundings.

'Darling!' His blue eyes brightened when he saw her. 'How's it going? Made any deals? Signed any million-dollar contracts?'

Alicia reached him, took his hand. 'David, I must ask a favour of you. I want to get Lindy away from Jean-Marc Brissac. He's in the drawing-room alone with her, and I think——'

'Do you have a business proposition for him?' David bit into his sandwich.

'No,' Alicia said grimly. 'This is personal. Lindy's hopelessly infatuated with him, and I'm afraid to leave her alone with him.'

'You mollycoddle that girl,' David said with a tone of great interest. 'I've noticed it before. You kiss her and call her baby—which is more than you do for me, God knows!' He smiled, blue eyes amused. 'Is that what you see in her, Alicia? A surrogate child?'

Alicia blanched, and said huskily, 'Well, if you won't help me get her away from him, I'll do it myself!' Turning, she walked away.

David leapt off the wall and ran after her. 'There's no need to go rampaging in on them like a defensive lioness protecting her cub!'

'Oh, you think I should let him seduce her again?'

'Again!' David's eyes widened, his hand shot out and caught her shoulder. 'Darling, you're not saying he's already——?'

'No.' Alicia's eyes blazed protectively. 'But...' Quickly, she outlined the few details Lindy had already told her.

'Oh, come on, Alicia!' David frowned. 'It's obvious what happened there! He was friendly to her, and she blew it up into a great big love-affair! It happens all the time.'

'Not to my niece!' she said thickly. 'Certainly not with the Last of the Great French Lovers!'

David shook his head, mouth compressing. 'Look—the guy's got more women than he knows what to do with. He owns half the banking world, invites heads of state back to his château for dinner parties, and almost married an Arabian princess last year. What in God's name do you think he'd see in a little doe-eyed kid like Lindy?'

'He was bored,' Alicia said anxiously. 'And she was around. That's what he saw in her, David, and that's what I want to prevent happening again.' There wasn't time to explain more, so she just walked from him into the drawing-room, her heart drumming with concern.

However, she found Lindy alone, in tears. Pausing in the doorway, her dark eyes flashed round the room, seeking Jean-Marc Brissac's ruthless face. He had gone.

'Is everything——?' David rushed up beside her, stopped, staring round the room, then clucked his tongue. 'Oh ... poor little Lindy!' He went over to her, putting his arms around her and hugging her to his chest.

Alicia turned, and her eyes were as black and fiery as burning coals as they flashed around the elegant garden, searching for him. She did not have to look hard.

Jean-Marc Brissac stood out from the pack, head and shoulders above every other man, his self-assurance and arrogant stance indicating a masculine authority that went beyond conceit and into the realms of formidable power.

His power over women was legendary. His power in the financial world was formidable. His power as a man was evident in every line of that hard handsome face and the steely grey eyes.

Alicia suddenly felt an urge so violent to break that power, to dent his colossal ego, and to knock some of that absolute self-assurance out of him, that she trembled visibly with it.

He tensed, sensing her gaze, and flashed his narrowed steel-grey eyes up to her face, but Alicia did not attempt to look away; she met that gaze power for power, and saw his black eyebrows rise sharply at the expression on her face.

David came up to her in the doorway. 'Darling, poor Lindy is——'

'Don't do that!' Alicia said huskily, pushing his embrace away. 'Just go and bring the car round! I want to get her out of here!'

'Darling, I know you're upset,' David touched her pale cheek, 'but Lindy will recover. We all do.'

'I want to leave,' Alicia said thickly, because of course she knew that wasn't true. We don't all recover, she thought, looking across the lawns at Jean-Marc Brissac.

Some of us never recover. Some of us are simply too vulnerable.

CHAPTER TWO

THE following week felt disrupted. Normally cool and efficient, Alicia found herself staring angrily at the designs on her desk, remembering Jean-Marc Brissac's ruthless face and the cold way he had dismissed poor Lindy once she had served her purpose. The days limped by, she found herself hurrying to match her usual pace and was almost completely left behind by Friday.

Her offices were in Kensington. Inheriting the building from her father at seventeen, she had known immediately that the small men's shirt manufacturer's business could be far more efficient and profitable as a fashionable women's boutique.

Alicia had always been artistic. When she lost her family and her capacity to believe in love it became her major outlet, and she became a fashion designer. She rose rapidly from a minor high-street boutique to a major force in fashion. Last year, at twenty-five, she had won the coveted award of Most Promising Newcomer to European Fashion.

The award stood in her office, on the black stone art deco mantelpiece, and, above it, a photograph of herself accepting it from Allie Makrett, the top designer in Europe.

On Friday afternoon, she found herself staring at that award and the photograph above it, remembering Lindy's words: 'Too beautiful to touch, too cold to marry, because you look after a career instead of love, marriage and children.'

Alicia shivered. The black and white checked Nicole Farhi mini-suit she wore was featured in this month's *Vogue*, and she looked devastatingly beautiful in it. But too beautiful to touch...?

When David arrived at six to pick her up, he said, 'Are you all right, darling? You seem rather preoccupied.'

'A hard day.' She slid into the front seat, a frown on her brow. 'David—do you think I'm too beautiful to touch?'

He laughed and started the engine. 'I certainly do not! Why do you ask?'

Her lashes flickered. 'Just something Lindy said to me.' She suddenly could no longer contain the feeling of restless dissatisfaction that had been eating at her all week. 'Darling—I want to get out of this city.'

He grinned. 'Is that an invitation for a dirty weekend?'

'Don't be ridiculous,' she said, lifting her brows coolly.

'Why is it ridiculous?' He gave a harsh sigh. 'We're engaged to be married, Alicia!'

'And will remain platonic until after the wedding.' Alicia shot him an uncertain look through her black lashes. 'I thought we'd agreed on that. I thought you understood.'

'I do, but...' He sighed. 'I just get so frustrated sometimes, darling. I feel as though I can't break through your reserve, no matter what I do.'

'My reserve...?' she queried.

He took her hand and kissed it. 'Your cold beauty, my darling. It really is quite awe-inspiring.'

She stared at him. 'But you've asked me to marry you and I've said yes! How can you consider me awe-inspiring?'

He shrugged, carried on driving. 'I feel I understand you. I feel I know why you're so—unapproachable. You're very ambitious, and you can't allow anything to get in the way of that. Certainly not love.'

Horrified, unable to continue the conversation in case he said anything even more damning than he had already said, Alicia changed the subject.

'Well, darling,' she said with a light smile, 'in that case, my idea of a short break away from work should be just what we need.'

He laughed. 'This really *is* an invitation for a dirty weekend!'

'No, it's not, David,' she said with affection, patting his hand. 'But it *is* an invitation to romance.'

'Sounds good to me!' David laughed. 'Where shall we go?'

'Paris,' Alicia said at once, and suddenly realised she had known that was where she wanted to go all along. She wondered why, but there was no answer. It was just a sudden deep yearning for the city of lovers . . .

They flew to Paris the next day. Arriving in the afternoon, they checked into the Paris Ritz, the chic palace on the Place Vendôme, surrounded by the legend of Cartier and the ghosts of Hemingway, Fitzgerald, Coco Chanel. They each had a suite, and Alicia didn't bat an eyelid as she gave the details of her gold Am-Ex card at the desk before taking both keys.

'I'll meet you in the bar for a drink,' she told David, 'in one hour. I'd like time to unpack and take a bath first.'

David followed her to the lift. 'I'd rather have drinks in my suite with you. Surely that's the point of this trip? A lot of luxury and a little romance...?'

Alicia pressed the call button with a polished nail. 'Darling, you know being alone together in either suite would be dangerous, and not at all suitable.'

'Romantic weekends,' said David with a frown, 'are supposed to be dangerous and unsuitable.'

'Not in my book!' Alicia frowned at him and stepped into the lift.

David pulled her back, his hand around her wrist. 'Alicia, for God's sake! You can't seriously expect me to keep my hands off you under these circumstances!'

Alicia prickled from head to foot, appalled at the scene he was on the point of creating in the luxurious foyer. 'David, please!'

'No,' he said firmly under his breath, 'I won't let you go! Not unless you agree to let me come to your suite!'

Alicia drew a level breath. Her face was flushed. She was acutely aware that people were watching and listening. Her dislike of public scenes was blackmail enough, and David knew it.

'Very well,' she said with a sigh, 'come to my room in one hour.' And she told him her suite number.

Turning on her impeccable Charles Jourdan heels, she walked into the lift and rode up to the seventh floor, frowning over his behaviour. Who would have thought David capable of creating a scene just to get his own way? He'd always been so sensitive and understanding.

When she entered the cool, calm luxury of her suite she threw her key down on the chaise-longue and went straight to the bathroom to switch on the bathtaps. The toiletries were arrayed in a wicker basket like an exclusive perfume counter. Alicia tipped designer bubble-bath into the rushing water, studied the expensive soap with indifference.

The porter delivered her Louis Vuitton suitcase. Alicia opened it, unpacked efficiently, then stripped off her clothes and walked nude to the bathroom.

David wouldn't arrive for at least another forty minutes. She sank into the scented water, closed her eyes, and came to terms with her folly in coming here.

That conversation with Lindy about Jean-Marc Brissac had upset her. Of that there was no longer any doubt. She'd felt troubled all week, haunted by her young niece's words, and, in a crazy bid to prove to herself that Lindy was wrong, she had asked David to come to Paris . . .

It was rapidly, however, becoming clear that she did not want romance with David. But why was she marrying him in that case? To have children? It had never occurred to her before that she might want children this badly. And if she did—how could she contemplate having them with a man she could not face making love with?

She had never pretended to be passionate. Certainly not with David. She had always made it clear, in the year they had been together, that she was first and foremost a businesswoman, in that most feminine of arenas—fashion. David had been head over heels in love with her, though, and his warmth and charm had eventually persuaded her that they had a chance of making a marriage work.

Without romance, though? Without physical affection? Alicia frowned and, at that second, the doorbell of the suite rang. Surely that couldn't be David!

Annoyed, Alicia got out of the bath, padded naked to the door and took the bath-robe, slipping into it, her face clean-scrubbed, her hair wet, the fluffy robe far too big for her.

As she wrenched open the door, her dark eyes flashed. 'David, if you think this is——' She broke off, gasping as she met a pair of steel-grey eyes that stopped her heart, took her breath away.

'Well, well, well,' Jean-Marc Brissac drawled softly, a mocking smile on his hard mouth as he ran his gaze over her with insolent sexual appraisal. 'The Snow Queen is human, after all!'

He was tall. At least six foot six, and the breadth of his shoulders was formidable. He wore a black suit, impeccably cut, and his grey eyes were making her heart thud faster and her face flush.

'You look distinctly *déshabillée, chérie*!' He smiled lazily. 'Are you expecting someone?'

Alicia tried to shut the door in his face, but he prevented her from doing so by putting one strong tanned hand on the panels and holding it steady as though he were a tank.

'Your boyish fiancé, perhaps?' he drawled. 'I heard you giving him his instructions in the foyer. He seemed most accommodating. Does he always do as he is told?' His grey eyes slid insolently to the neck of her robe as he added mockingly, 'Or perhaps he is your employee—not your lover?'

She could barely breathe, conscious of her dishevelled appearance and the stark sense of vulnerability she felt but, most of all, conscious of the way this man made the hair on the back of her neck prickle with a hostility she had never felt before.

'Get away from this door!' she said in breathless rage. 'Before I call security!'

'There is no need for security,' he said softly, watching her. 'I merely wanted to see what you would look like without your armour.'

He moved away from the door just as Alicia slammed it. Heart thudding violently, she just stood there, shaking like a leaf.

His insults rang in her ears. She struggled for coherent thought, reminding herself that he was ruthless, calculating, and would use any trick at his disposal to get what he wanted.

Breathing erratically, Alicia went into her bedroom to dress. Jean-Marc Brissac had obviously felt insulted by her behaviour towards him at the garden party.

She stared at her hands. She was still shaking.

Dressing in a formal black skirt suit, Alicia deliberately made herself look as coolly elegant as possible. If David was coming here with seduction on his mind, an exterior of aristocratic reserve was the safest device she could use to defuse his desire. Coiling her glossy black hair into a severe chignon, she applied red lipstick to her mouth, black liner to her wide dark eyes, and pearl earrings to her lobes.

When the doorbell rang at ten past three, she was ready, strolling immaculately dressed to the door, tall and strikingly beautiful in her high black heels.

Jean-Marc Brissac.

Her eyes widened in shock and she tried to slam the door, but he pushed it open, shouldering in, a mocking smile on his hard mouth, to close the door behind him and lean against it.

Waves of angry panic engulfed her. She was staring at him, lips parted, barely able to breathe.

'Your fiancé is downstairs in the bar,' Jean-Marc Brissac drawled softly, watching her through heavy eyelids. 'I gave him your message.'

'What message?' she asked, her voice shaking with alarm.

'That a business problem had arisen,' he drawled sardonically. 'And that you were unavoidably detained until four o'clock.'

She stared, dark eyes blazing. 'You told him that!'

'He was surprised, of course,' he murmured, unsmiling, 'but he understood, and had a polite conversation with me about my financial interests. I bought him a drink, and left him in the bar.'

'I don't believe you!' she said through taut lips.

'Yes, you do,' he said with a lift of arrogant brows. 'That's why you're so angry.' He smiled, straightening suddenly, and walking coolly towards her. 'And so afraid.'

'I'm not afraid!' she denied hotly, and backed from him, her sense of panic making her breathe erratically, staring up at him with eyes that were stretched wide, her mouth reflecting her acute tension.

'He's a charming boy,' Jean-Marc Brissac commented, allowing his grey gaze to slide coolly over her body. 'But he's no match for you. Is he, Alicia?'

She lifted her head. 'My relationship with David is none of your business!'

'Apparently none of his business, either,' he drawled softly, sliding his hands into the pockets of his beautifully cut black trousers, his jacket apart, drawing her eye helplessly to the powerful male chest in the tight black waistcoat, and the sheer stark masculinity of his stance. 'I've never been so amused by a couple before. You strode into the hotel with that boy, paid for the rooms, gave him his orders, and then dismissed him.'

'How dare you?' she burst out, and suddenly knew she wanted to slap his hard arrogant face, because what he had said was so unacceptable to her, but, at the same time, so horribly close to the truth.

'How long have you been engaged to him?' he asked, dark brows rising in commanding enquiry.

'Six months!' she snapped hotly. 'Not that it's any of your——'

'A beautiful woman like you?' he cut in, eyes narrowed. 'Is that really the best you could do?'

'My God,' she breathed, shaking with rage, 'you insolent swine! How dare you come here and lecture me on my private life?'

'Perhaps I think it's time someone did,' he said softly, letting his grey eyes drift over her slender hipbones to the long, toned lines of her legs encased in sheer black tights. 'Perhaps I think it's time someone taught you what love between a man and a woman should be.'

Hot colour flooded her neck and face in a tidal wave, ruining her aristocratic reserve, making her heart hammer as she saw the cool smile on his hard mouth as he noted the intensely female reaction.

'Certainly,' he said, moving towards her, 'your obedient boyfriend won't be the one to teach you!'

She took a backward step, came into contact with the pale green couch, and was forced to stand her ground, but her heart was hammering and the alarm she felt went right to the deepest level of her.

'Come a step closer,' she whispered, 'and I'll scream!'

Eyes insolent, he stepped closer, a smile on his hard mouth, a look of mocking intent in his grey eyes as he gauged correctly the chaos he was invoking in her. He laughed sardonically. 'Never make a threat unless you can carry it through, Alicia.' His strong hands slid slowly on to her narrow waist.

'Get your hands off me!' she choked out.

'Men and women are such different creatures,' he drawled lazily. 'Man is the hunter. Woman the prey. Any other way simply does not work, *chérie*. Reverse the roles at your peril.'

'This is the late twentieth century,' she said hoarsely, struggling to retain some wit and dignity, 'not the neanderthal era!'

'Some things,' he said mockingly, 'never change.' He pulled her against his hard body until she could feel every inch of it, her pulses beating so fast that she was incapable of speech, just staring at his hard face and feeling the blood pulsate through her body.

He was watching her face, his eyes ruthless, and she started to struggle, at last, fear driving her to break out of her own armour as she fought him, gasping hotly, her face scarlet and her dark eyes filled with stark terror.

Forcing her struggling body down on to the couch, he was unstoppable, his face hard as he imposed his powerful body and sheer male strength at will, and the panic throbbed in her veins as she twisted beneath him, breath coming in hoarse gasps as he held her pinned and his eyes focused on her trembling mouth.

'Please...' she whispered shakingly, and he looked so different from this angle, his black hair falling across his tanned forehead, his tough face filled with a sexual impact that made her whole body tremble in violent response.

As his hard mouth closed over hers Alicia renewed her struggles, and he reasserted his superiority by clamping her in position, his hands firm on her wrists, pinning them either side of her head. Her breasts rose and fell with panic as the sensations filled her, sensations she had never before experienced as he forced her to accept the brutal, savage domination of his kiss.

'Stop fighting me!' he bit out coldly against her mouth. 'Or I'll lose my temper.'

Her breath caught at the implicit threat, and she felt the fight go out of her, her mouth opening helplessly beneath his as his domination of her became complete.

Mindless, boneless, she was incapable of stopping him, her eyes closed and her mouth bruised with passion as she received his kisses, heart thudding at the feel of those hard thighs pressing inexorably against her and that powerful chest covering hers so completely.

When his strong hand slid up over her body to slowly cup her breast she moaned hoarsely, more helpless than ever, feeling his mouth come softly away from hers as he studied her with narrowed eyes for a second, then stroked her breast slowly, watching her as she stared helplessly into his tough face, her heart pounding like a violent drum beneath his long fingers, lost in the hot whirlpool of sensual excitement he had inflicted so forcefully on her.

Suddenly, his mouth was sliding over her throat and she felt his strong hands unbuttoning with slow, expert skill the front of her black suit, sliding the crisp, elegant jacket apart while she kissed his hard mouth, her hands moving up with unconscious submission to his broad shoulders, and then his neck, and then pushing into his black hair.

He stroked her bare stomach lightly with his fingers and she felt her head begin to reel as she gasped helplessly beneath him, feeling those fingers move up to her breast, caressing it through the black lace bra that now seemed so exciting, so erotic, so feminine to her...

The knock at the door made no impact on Alicia. She was lost to reality, submerged in a tide of primitive response to his brutal male strength, and when he lifted his dark head from hers she was shocked, felt deprived, opening her wild dark eyes with a wrench.

In the silence, he studied her passionate face, from the bruised red mouth to the flush on her cheeks and the fevered darkness of her eyes. Of course, she didn't understand why he had stopped, and just gazed at him helplessly, trembling in the grip of her hunger.

The knock came again.

'Your fiancé, I imagine,' Jean-Marc said with a wry smile, 'Come to see if you've got time for him yet.'

Alicia stared at him, appalled, struggling to think as the mist of desire faded and reality punched a hole through the veil, making her give a hoarse cry, sitting up, shaking as she struggled to button up her black jacket.

Jean-Marc watched her with a sardonic grin. 'Modesty! A little late for my benefit, don't you think?'

She shot him a look of pure hatred. 'You did this deliberately... came here deliberately... you want to ruin my engagement to David!'

'I think that's taking things a little too far, Alicia,' he said flatly. 'I think it also shows a trace of displaced hostility. You're angry because you lost your head. Don't take it out on me.'

'Who else am I supposed to take it out on?' she hissed, standing up, her shaking hands struggling to repair her chignon into its customary severity. 'You could destroy what little trust David now has in me!'

'If your engagement is on the rocks, Alicia,' he said coolly, 'it's because something is wrong between you and that boy. My presence here won't save it or destroy it.'

The knock came again. 'Alicia?' David's voice said in the corridor.

She froze, staring in horror at Jean-Marc. 'What am I going to do?'

'I don't know,' he replied calmly, lounging on the sofa, his red silk tie loosened, black hair tousled from her caresses, lipstick on his tanned cheek. 'What do you want to do?'

'Don't be so insensitive!' she said hoarsely. 'He's my fiancé and I love him! How can I let him in here with you . . . lying there like that?' The reality of what had happened sank in and she covered her face with her hands, shaking.

Outside, the sound of David's retreating footsteps made the decision for her. She listened, her hands gradually leaving her face. Then she looked down at Jean-Marc Brissac with a bitter expression.

'Get out!' she said, and her voice was raw with emotion, her dark eyes blazing with it, her legs shaking beneath her. In just a few short minutes, this man had knocked her off balance in every area, leaving her feeling almost naked with vulnerability.

He smiled, swung his long legs off the *chaise-longue*, straightening with a ripple of muscle beneath the formal black suit that made her mouth go dry.

'As you wish,' he drawled, grey eyes mocking as he towered over her. 'But thank you for such an interesting revelation. You're quite a woman underneath that cold, aristocratic exterior. I wish I had more time to completely obliterate your considerable defences. Unfortunately, I have an appointment, too.' He ran one long finger to her trembling mouth. 'Perhaps some other time?'

'Get out!' she spat, shaking, and he strode coolly to the door, closing it behind him with a quiet click that only underlined his complete masculine self-assurance.

Only when he had gone did she realise her legs were shaking too much to enable her to stand. Stumbling into her bedroom, she sank on to the bed, staring at her hands, appalled by the seemingly unstoppable tremor in them.

David would be waiting for her in the bar. She couldn't just sit here forever, cursing Jean-Marc Brissac. He had blown a hole in her defences, and she remembered her helpless passion in his arms with bitter self-loathing.

But she mustn't think about that now! Forcing herself to stand, she went to the dressing-table, sank down in front of it, and began to repair her make-up.

Minutes later, she walked into the bar, the picture of cold aristocratic elegance, her black hair pulled back into its severe chignon, black suit drawing admiring glances from men as she looked around the room for David's reassuring blond head.

'Darling!' He got to his feet as he saw her, greeted her with a kiss on her high, slanting cheekbone, and offered her the opposite seat. 'What can I get you? The barman, Michel, assures me that his *champagne fraise* is the best in all Paris!'

Alicia smiled, sinking down into the comfortable dark armchair. 'That sounds lovely. Our first day in Paris...'

'Yes, what shall we do this afternoon?' He glanced at his watch. 'It's almost four. I thought a horse and carriage ride would be romantic. And it's very sunny out there.'

'Why not?' She was keen to join David in romantic pastimes now, feeling shaky as a person, a fiancée, and especially as a woman. 'And we can talk as we go, can't we? We need to talk more, David.' Her hand somehow found its way to close over his in an affectionate touch. 'You're right. Our romance has been postponed for too long.'

Astonished, he stared, then smiled, saying, 'Darling, I can't tell you how overjoyed I am to hear you say that! It's been——'

'Good afternoon,' drawled a terrifyingly familiar voice behind her. 'I'm not intruding, am I?'

Turning her dark head, she stared with stricken eyes into Jean-Marc Brissac's hard face and felt her heart plummet as though in a lift shaft, her legs instantly beginning to tremble.

'Not at all,' David was saying in his best accent, 'we're just having a drink before going out. Won't you join us? What will you have?'

'Thank you.' A sardonic smile touched his hard mouth as he glanced at Alicia through those heavy lids. 'A whisky. On the rocks.'

As he sank down beside Alicia, he was smiling faintly, mockery in his steel-grey eyes, and she avoided his glance, hating him with the most overpowering wave of rage she had ever felt in her life. How dared he intrude like this? He knew perfectly well he was butting in to a private conversation.

'Interesting that we should run into each other again so swiftly,' Jean-Marc drawled coolly.

'Yes, isn't it?' David was beckoning the barman and giving the order. 'When was that party, Alicia?'

'Last weekend,' she said stiffly.

'I enjoy my interests in the fashion world.' Brissac flicked his cool grey gaze to Alicia and added softly, 'I like to keep my finger on the pulse—particularly when it starts to throb.'

She tightened her mouth and looked away, a hot tide of colour sweeping up her neck and face.

'Of course,' Brissac said, 'it's an industry like any other. There's a lot of money in it. But for me, it is a self-indulgence. A multi-million-dollar enterprise filled with beautiful women.' He smiled, his grey eyes mocking as they ran coolly over Alicia's tense body. 'And your fiancée is without doubt one of the most beautiful. I've seen her work. Passionate and intensely feminine.'

Alicia stared at her glass of *champagne fraise*.

'So surprising,' he added softly, 'given her very cool façade.'

'You just don't know Alicia,' David assured him with a friendly smile. 'She channels all her energies into her work—don't you, darling?'

She could have killed him for saying that, her dark eyes flashing up to his face in brief warning, and the look of hurt surprise he gave her made her feel worse.

'Really?' Jean-Marc Brissac studied her bent head with sardonic amusement. 'You don't feel you ought to strike a balance, then, Mademoiselle Alicia?'

She gave him a look of intense hatred. 'I feel I ought to strike something!'

'I quite agree,' he said softly, 'and I have the perfect solution.' Reaching into his black-silk-lined inside jacket pocket, he produced a card. 'A friend of mine is having a party tonight. It's at a private house in the Bois de Boulogne. Here is the address.' He put the card on the marble-topped table and pushed it coolly, with one finger, towards her. 'I would be delighted if you would both attend.'

She stared at the card as though it were a hot snake.

'That's very kind of you!' David reached for the card. 'Impressive address! We'd be honoured to attend—wouldn't we, darling?'

Her stricken expression amused Brissac as she struggled not to betray her chaotic emotions, her dark eyes almost pleading as she said thickly, 'David——'

'Nine o'clock, then?' Brissac interrupted her coolly.

'Yes, we'll be there,' David said, throwing a frowning look at Alicia. 'Although we won't be able to stay long. We are, after all, here for a romantic weekend.'

Her cheeks burned like fire at that.

'A romantic weekend?' Brissac enquired with a lift of sardonic brows. 'Roses, moonlight and a fast-beating heart!'

'That's the kind of thing!' David laughed.

'Well, we in France approve of love and lovers,' Brissac said with soft threat implicit in his ruthless eyes. 'And if you attend this party, *mademoiselle*, I shall personally see to it that your heart beats very fast indeed!'

David barely heard, sipping his drink, and Alicia stared at Brissac with rage smouldering in her dark eyes.

Brissac got to his feet, leaving his whisky untouched. 'Until tonight, then. *Au revoir à toute à l'heure.*' Turning, he strode with lazy arrogance away from their table and out of the bar.

'Why did you accept that invitation?' Alicia asked tightly, chaotic emotion running riot in her. 'Why did you do it?'

CHAPTER THREE

DAVID was genuinely hurt, and Alicia was consumed with guilt. He had no idea of the ordeal Jean-Marc Brissac had put her through, or of her intense hatred for him: a hatred which seemed to rage out of control whenever she thought of his mocking, arrogant, ruthless face.

They went for their carriage ride in the sunlit afternoon. Paris was idyllic, filled with beautiful women dressed in floaty summer dresses, the Seine a tree-lined mirage of blue-gold dappled water as the horses clip-clopped beside it and David held her hand in the comfortable seat of the polished wooden carriage.

'I honestly didn't realise you disliked him that much,' he said again, frowning. 'If I'd known, I would have politely refused.'

Alicia sighed, eyes flickering with concern over his face. 'I know. And I'm sorry I reacted so badly. It was just because I didn't feel able to say anything...not in front of him.'

He laughed. 'But you're usually so formidable! Why did you feel bound by courtesy?'

'Because of what he did to Lindy!' Alicia explained hotly, desperate to believe her own lie. 'I believed it when she first told me—and I believe it even more now that I've met him properly.'

'Oh, come on!' David said with his customary bluntness. 'From the very biased details of Lindy's

37

story, it was just a simple case of infatuation that ended in tears.'

'She was very badly hurt!' Alicia protested.

'She'll get over it.' He sighed and shook his blond head as the carriage rolled with stately slowness into the cobbled courtyard of the Louvre. 'Darling, let's just forget Brissac and enjoy Paris. Look at all this . . . it's so beautiful.'

'Must we go to this party, then?'

'Well, we can't deliberately not turn up.' He lifted blond brows. 'It would be a gratuitous insult. Jean-Marc Brissac may or may not be an absolute bastard where women are concerned, but he is most certainly a very powerful man. You mustn't make an enemy of him.'

'I wouldn't give a damn!' Alicia broke out hotly, dark eyes smouldering.

'Of course you would.' David frowned. 'Darling, this isn't like you. You're a stickler for not letting something personal intrude on business. Brissac could do you a lot of harm just by lifting a finger and pointing it at you. Don't insult the man. Don't risk getting annihilated just because your niece got hurt.'

Alicia suddenly felt alarmed, because she knew he was right. This wasn't like her. Jean-Marc Brissac's ruthless skill as a lover had completely thrown her off balance. That she now believed every word of Lindy's story went without saying. Just imagining what he had put her poor, innocent niece through made her angry. Knowing what he had just put *her* through—well, it made smoke come out of her ears.

'All right,' she said quietly, struggling to remain sane where Brissac was concerned. 'We'll go to the party.'

'That's my girl!' David said with a smile, and pulled her into his arms, kissing her mouth, his eyes dancing. 'We'll go along, leave after an hour, and never see him again.'

They spent the rest of the afternoon shopping lazily. Alicia was able gradually to forget her rage with Brissac, and the shaking incident in her hotel room. She bought a beautiful porcelain doll for Lindy, taking care to ensure it was not a childish one, but as she carried it back along the hot, beautiful cobbled street to the Ritz, she knew it had been the wrong present.

'I don't think I'll give this to Lindy,' she said quietly to David as they strolled hand in hand past Cartier.

'Why not?' He took the package, studied the exquisite black-haired porcelain doll. 'It's ravishing. And you always bring presents back for her when you travel.'

'Yes . . .' Alicia's dark eyes reflected hurt. 'But she told me off the other day for calling her baby. I don't see that a doll would be——'

'Did she?' David nodded, kissed her cheek. 'Well, she's seventeen now, darling. And she's not your daughter: just your niece.'

Alicia lowered her lashes and changed the subject, but she felt a deep sense of loss at the thought of not being able to indulge Lindy any more. A door was being closed, one that might never open again, and it made her see how much she had needed Lindy.

As they went into the hotel, her heart gave a jolt when she saw Jean-Marc Brissac standing in the foyer talking to a stunning blonde, his grey eyes sardonically inspecting her mouth as she pouted and laughed, throwing him adoring looks.

Jealous rage shot through Alicia, and her eyes clashed with his as he turned to look at her. Deliberately, she flicked him a look of haughty contempt and walked past him with her head held high.

In the lift, she jabbed the button, saying tightly, 'He really is the Last of the Great French Lovers, isn't he? Did you see that woman throwing herself at him?'

David laughed. 'Yes! Lucky swine! Mind you— he really has got it, hasn't he? Money, power, good looks and sex appeal in lethal doses! Who gave him that title, though? Wasn't it *Life* magazine? About ten years ago?'

'I don't know and I don't care!' Alicia snapped, pulses thudding with a renewal of rage. 'I just want to get this party over and done with and never have to see his arrogant face again.'

Later, as she got dressed in her room, she prayed it would be that easy.

They drove out to the Bois in an air-conditioned Citroën taxi. Alicia had taken great care with her clothes and make-up. The stark white shift dress she wore was the most stunning in her wardrobe. Made of silk, it clung to every curve, covered in an identical piece of white chiffon sewn in scattered patterns with tiny silver sequins. The neck was high, but the back was low, and her slender spine was revealed in sensual elegance, as were her long slender legs, silver evening shoes completing the outfit.

'You're quite breathtaking, Alicia,' David said softly in the back of the taxi, staring at her beautiful face. 'I'm so proud to be engaged to you. I can't believe you'll one day be my wife! It's just a dream come true...'

Alicia smiled, and when he kissed her in the dark interior of the taxi she felt a stab of anxiety, because her body was unresponsive to his touch. No pulses leapt, no fire burned and no emotion other than warm affection filled her.

She had always known David loved her more than she loved him. But she had never realised there was anything wrong with that. She intended to marry him, she felt a deep affection for him, and she did not want any drama or excitement in her personal life.

She certainly did not want a man like Brissac to show her so forcefully that she was capable of feeling it.

The Bois was deliciously elegant, scattered with moonlight and lush trees, lakes and parks, and curving rows of big, elegant houses. The house the party was held in was exceptionally beautiful, and the row of luxury cars outside it signified the calibre of the guests.

'God, this is fantastic!' David stared up at the place, shaking his head. 'Like something out of a film.'

Alicia nodded vaguely, walking up the path, saying, 'Hmm...' Inside, she was filled with tense apprehension at the thought of seeing Brissac.

The front door was opened by a butler in uniform, who showed them in to the elegant house and led them to the sound of music and voices in the luxurious drawing-room.

'Oh, my God!' David caught his breath, staring, whispering, 'It's Isabelle Janvier...!'

Alicia's dark eyes were darting around in search of Brissac.

Isabelle Janvier, the French film star, turned her cool blonde head and regarded them with ice-cold blue eyes, her white skin translucent and perfect as porcelain.

'*Monsieur Balham,*' intoned the butler to Isabelle Janvier, '*et Mademoiselle Holt.*'

Those famous crystalline eyes flickered blankly over their faces. '*Je ne suis pas sûre qui——*'

'My guests,' cut in a cool, heart-stopping male voice. '*Je m'excuse*, Isabelle. I did tell you they would arrive.'

Alicia gave him a dark, smouldering look of hatred, her head held high with haughty contempt as she met his gun-metal-grey eyes and felt the physical impact of his presence like a blow to the solar plexus.

He introduced them to their hostess, who gave one of her famous cool smiles and beckoned a waiter to bring them champagne.

'Alicia is a fashion designer,' Jean-Marc Brissac told his mistress. 'You have one or two of her designs in your wardrobe.'

'*Ah, oui.*' Isabelle smiled with cool interest. 'A red silk dress and a silver blouse. I like your work. It is chic, feminine, sexy... are you in Paris on business?'

'Pleasure,' Jean-Marc Brissac drawled sardonically before she could answer. 'She wants to lose her head in the city of lovers!'

Her eyes flashed at him. 'My fiancé and I wanted to spend some time alone together,' she told Isabelle. 'He thinks I work too hard.'

David was silent at her side, agog with admiration for Isabelle.

'I work too hard,' Brissac said coolly, grey eyes flickering over Alicia's slender shape in the dazzling dress and invoking shivers of angry response as his eyes stripped her with slow insolent mockery. 'But I know how to play hard, too, and this is the key to fulfilment. We all need to find fulfilment— don't we, Alicia?'

Alicia burnt with rage at the provocative double-talk, only too well aware of his true meaning. But even though she gave him hostile, icy looks of aristocratic hauteur, the mocking look in his eyes dissolved her weapons with stark penetration.

'Oh . . . !' Isabelle Janvier said after a whispered aside from the butler. 'The fireworks are ready. Won't you come outside?'

David's blue eyes lit up. 'Fireworks! Wow...' He followed Isabelle, naturally assuming Alicia would follow too.

'Not that way.' Jean-Marc Brissac caught her arm in a vice-like grip as she began to walk away. 'I want to speak to you privately before we watch the fireworks.'

'Go to hell!' she said through her teeth, glaring up at him.

'Such cool courtesy, Alicia!' he drawled with soft mockery. 'Where is the Snow Queen now?'

'Marshalling her forces!' she snapped.

'Have I scattered them, *chérie*?' he murmured.

'No, you have not!' she said angrily. 'I just didn't expect to have to fight when I arrived here! This is a romantic weekend for me!'

'Not any more,' he drawled. 'From the minute I kissed you this afternoon, it became war. Our war, Alicia. Our private war...'

Alicia stared at him, a pulse beating in her throat. Guests were moving all around them, filtering across to the french windows, the lights on the terrace illuminating the manicured gardens.

'This way,' Brissac murmured, leading her away before she could stop and think.

'Let go of my arm!' Alicia snapped, appalled as he got her to a door and pushed it open. 'What do you think you're doing?'

'Dominating you!' he drawled, pushing her forcibly into the warm dark red study and slamming the door behind them before she could get away.

Heart thudding in her mouth, she stared at him, every instinct in her clamouring to start screaming and run from him as if he were the devil. But pride and courage made her stand her ground.

'David will be worried,' she said tightly. 'He'll put two and two together.'

'An interesting English phrase,' he said calmly. 'I know another: marriage of convenience.'

She caught her breath at his insolence. 'Are you suggesting I'm not in love with my fiancé?'

'I'm not suggesting it. I'm stating it directly.'

Fuming, she snapped, 'You really are an insolent bastard!'

'It's one of my charms,' he drawled, a smile on his hard mouth as he let his grey eyes slide with implicit sexual threat over her body. 'Want me to illustrate it more forcefully?'

'No...' she said shakily, taking an instinctive step back.

He smiled and walked towards her. 'You know, it interests me that a woman of your drives and abilities could waste herself on a man who can only stand back and watch while you scale the heights to even greater ambition.'

'You know nothing about my relationship with David!' she said bitterly. 'Kindly mind your own business!'

'But it is my business, Alicia,' he said softly, backing her up against the leather-topped desk while she stared up at him, her pulses throbbing. 'This is war, remember? You're under attack—or haven't you noticed?'

Eyes stricken, she said hoarsely, 'I have no quarrel with you!'

'Liar!' he said under his breath, grey eyes gleaming. 'Do you think I can't sense your hatred? When we were at that garden party last week, I walked into the drawing-room and found you with my goddaughter's friend, and I could feel your rage crackling across the room at me like electricity.'

Dry-mouthed, she whispered, 'I don't want to talk about it!'

'You were deliberately insulting,' he said flatly. 'You snubbed me. You walked out of the room as though I were a messenger-boy, and made me feel completely irrelevant.' He gave a slow, mocking laugh. 'I was intrigued, to say the least.'

'I can assure you I had no intention of intriguing you!'

'I watched you with your fiancé,' he said coolly. 'I knew straight away who was in charge of that little relationship. I felt sorry for him. He's a very ordinary young man, isn't he? Warm, cheerful and with no real ambition. Yet he's hopelessly in love with a cold, brilliant, ambitious woman. Perhaps he doesn't want to be loved.'

'Shut up!' she said, bitter dislike in her dark eyes. 'David doesn't see me like that! He loves me!'

'He worships you,' Brissac said cuttingly. 'That isn't the same thing.'

'He does not worship me!'

'Then why is he afraid of you?' he asked softly, and she could not reply. 'He never kisses you properly, does he, Alicia?' His grey eyes slid to her red mouth. 'He wouldn't dare inflict real passion on you.' One strong hand moved to her narrow waist. 'He'd never dream, for instance, of treating you as a woman!'

'Get your filthy hands off me!' she spat, breasts rising and falling as she felt those hard thighs pressing against her.

'I liked you best when I'd finished kissing you this afternoon, *chérie*,' he said with soft mockery. 'When you were all woman. Your mouth bruised and your eyes wild and your body quite helpless!'

'You mean you enjoy imposing your sadistic will on me!' she broke out hoarsely, her hands flying to his broad, powerful shoulders and pushing at them uselessly.

'I love it!' he drawled mockingly, and as his hard mouth closed over hers she was already giving a hoarse cry of angry excitement, feeling his hard thighs pressing against hers forcefully, holding her captive.

She fought him, bitterly, her hands raining blows on his broad shoulders and arrogant face. He caught her hands easily, pinned them behind her back with one hand, and his other hand moved swiftly to her face, forcing her to accept his kiss.

Drowning in hot waves of pleasure, she gave a harsh cry of unwilling submission and felt her mouth open beneath that hard, driving pressure.

He thrust a hand in her glossy black hair, pulling pins out of it impatiently, making it tumble around her flushed face and tilting her head back to receive his kiss, exerting his authority over her with ease until she was breathless, dizzy, her legs shaking beneath her.

When his hands slid over the naked warmth of her spine, she moaned, eyes closed to everything but that stark masculine domination and the hard mouth that moved so forcefully over hers. Her heart was beating like a drum. Blood was singing in her ears. She felt alive, coursing with primitive emotion, her arms now tightly wound around his neck as she gave soft, helpless moans of pleasure at the feel of his strong hands moving down over her hips.

He released her suddenly, scrutinising her dazed face with narrowed eyes, and Alicia swayed with a hoarse gasp, barely able to support herself, ruined by his lovemaking, her hair a wild cloud of black silk around her flushed and passionate face.

'Yes,' he said under his breath, as though answering a question.

Alicia struggled to retain her poise, but of course it was in ruins on the floor at his feet, obliterated by the sheer impact of his powerful sexuality.

Jean-Marc Brissac stepped back, thrusting his hands into the pockets of that impeccable black evening suit, every inch the man of power and legend as he watched her through those ruthless, heavy-lidded eyes.

'I have a proposition for you,' he said coolly.

Her wild dark eyes flashed to his face. 'I can guess!'

A smile indented the hard mouth. 'Not that kind of proposition. Although I would be tempted, given your very exciting submission.'

'My God, you bastard!' she said, shaking, deeply conscious of her total vulnerability to him, standing here barely able to support herself after the impact of his kiss, her face flushed, her eyes dark pools of fire, her mouth bruised and her hair a cloud of silk around her shaking shoulders.

He laughed. 'You really are falling to pieces at my hands, aren't you? If only your fiancé could see you now!'

She glared at him, not trusting herself to speak.

'My goddaughter is getting married shortly,' he said coolly, startling her. 'I'm hosting the wedding at my château in the Loire. I want you to design and make her dress, all the bridesmaids' dresses, and basically give the occasion some fashionable style and gloss.'

'What?' Alicia stared at him. 'Are you completely insane? Why on earth should I do any of that?'

'Because I'll pay you to,' he said with a sardonic lift of his dark brows. 'That's why.'

Her mouth shook, dark eyes wild with emotion. 'Don't think I can't guess what you really want me there for! You've made your dishonourable intentions only too obvious!'

'I need someone to do the job,' he said flatly, mouth hard. 'I can't possibly do it myself. I'm too busy. Besides, I have no artistic flair for that kind of thing. My goddaughter wants her wedding to be the most fashionable of the year. Not only the dresses, but in every detail, from the ballroom décor to the invitations, the band that's hired, the Press reception ... everything.'

'I don't see where I fit in!' she said tightly.

He shrugged broad shoulders. 'You're at the centre of fashion, and you have a natural grasp of the spirit of the current era. What better choice could I make?'

'Another designer?' she said tautly. 'Someone you weren't at war with?'

The grey eyes flashed to hers. 'Ah ... so you accept that we are at war, now?'

Hot colour flooded her face. 'No, I do not! And I most certainly don't accept that I have any motive for accepting this "job" from you!'

'Don't be stupid, Alicia,' he said flatly. 'You must know the wedding will be featured in every magazine and newspaper in the western world. Not only will you be paid handsomely for your services—you will also make a bigger name for yourself and meet a lot of important new people into the bargain.'

Temptation stretched out to her and she hesitated, staring at him through her dark lashes, knowing she was in danger not only of accepting the job but of actively wanting it. If it was handled well, it would put her name in the same élite bracket as royal designers, and that was something that only came along to the lucky few.

'You'd enjoy it,' Brissac said softly, eyes narrowed on her flushed face as he sensed weakness. 'Think of the challenge, Alicia! Designing everything to reflect the era, and adding your own inimitable style.'

Angrily, she resisted, saying, 'Find someone else! I'm not interested in having to fend you off every night!'

'It would only be for two weeks,' he said at once. 'And I assure you I would not jeopardise my goddaughter's happiness by seducing the woman she needs to make her wedding dreams come true.'

Alicia looked away at the mention of his goddaughter, then said thickly, 'Your goddaughter... is it Dominique Dusort?'

He inclined his dark head.

'Isn't she a little young to be getting married?'

'I think so,' he said with a lazy shrug. 'But she is eighteen and a little spoilt, both by her father and by me. We have both tried to argue her out of this step, but she is adamant—and very deeply in love.'

Alicia's dark eyes moved restlessly over his strong face. 'Is she your only goddaughter?'

'Yes.' His hard mouth crooked in a smile. 'And I am ashamed to admit I dote on her. But I have no family now, and I've spent my life in the pursuit of power. Dominique is the daughter of my oldest friend, and I am very pleased that he agreed to let me host the wedding.'

This showed a side of him she had not expected, and she was unable to prevent the rise of understanding inside her as she examined his feelings for Dominique and saw the clear parallel with herself and Lindy.

But she could not risk another display of his powerful sexuality, and her own chaotic response to it. It was blatantly obvious that he would continue to wage sexual war on her if she went to the château, and only a fool would deny it.

'I'm sorry,' she said flatly, irritated by the regret she felt, 'but I can't accept the job.' Pushing away from the desk, she walked towards the door, her black hair tumbling like silk down her bare back.

Jean-Marc Brissac stopped her, a hand on her arm. 'I'll pay you well,' he said flatly, and named a figure which literally took her breath away.

'That's a king's ransom!' she said breathlessly, staring.

'My goddaughter is worth it,' he said, mouth hard. 'And I will give you twenty-four hours to think it over.'

'I don't need twenty-four hours!' she said, eyes sparking with anger. 'I've given you my answer— no!'

'Alicia,' he said softly, 'I have overridden the word no with you before. I'd love to do it again!' His gaze slid insolently to her bruised mouth. 'Would you love it, too?'

Her red mouth parted at his arrogance, and she wrenched open the door, saying shakily, 'No, I damned well would not!'

'Then say yes,' he murmured, running a hand over her cheek. 'I'll want my answer tomorrow.'

Storming away from him across the now darkened drawing-room, her heart thudded at a terrific pace, and her eyes stared straight ahead, filled with the wild smoulder of a Spanish gypsy, her red mouth and loose, flowing black hair attracting startled looks of sheer sexual attraction as she walked.

The guests were clustered in the doorway, drinking champagne, and as they parted to let her through without having to measure her pace, she saw David.

'I want to leave,' she said as she reached him.

'But I was just beginning to enjoy myself!' He smiled, then a frown touched his smooth brow. 'Why is your hair loose? What's happened . . . ?'

'My hair . . .' She flushed, suddenly realising how her looks betrayed her. 'I felt a little dizzy—thought it might help if I let my hair down.' How she hated herself for those white lies! But they were close to the truth, weren't they? 'Please, David. I really want to go . . .'

They went into the hall and rang for a taxi. Alicia spoke excellent French—Paris was the centre of fashion, and she had spent more time here than she could remember. The taxi arrived within minutes, and she was glad to escape without seeing Brissac again.

The Ritz looked lovely under the moon. The curve of the Place Vendôme was cobbled, Cartier gleamed with discreet élitism, and the statue of Napoleon looked down in haunting silence.

'It's early yet,' David said as they alighted from the taxi. 'Let's go for a walk. It'll be romantic.'

They strolled around Paris hand in hand. Alicia took her shoes off, walking barefoot alongside David, aware deep inside her that the romance was completely exterior. The moon, the Tuileries Gardens, the beautiful shops along the Rue de Rivoli. They reached the Place de la Concorde, and there was romance, lit up in classical statues of white stone, fountains spraying against a backdrop of Paris in the summer.

But inside, romance did not exist. Alicia sat on the edge of a fountain, watching David's face as he talked, and knew suddenly that she was capable of great passion—and that she would never feel it for David.

However much she hated Jean-Marc Brissac, he still brought her alive, made her feel sensations she had never experienced before. Those violent waves of passion she felt when he kissed her might not be love—but they were closer to that emotion than anything David had ever made her feel.

How could she marry David, knowing she could never give him the love he deserved to have? Kind, loving, considerate David. How could she condemn him to a slow dawning of awareness, a slow realisation that she would never respond in his arms?

I can't marry him, she thought, and was appalled.

I must not marry him.

'Let's come here on our honeymoon!' David swung to her with a broad smile, hands in his jacket pockets. 'I feel so wonderful tonight, Alicia. I want to remember this when we're married.'

Her face was pale and grave. 'David...' She reached out for his hand, her eyes filled with concern. 'Sit down beside me.'

David frowned, sinking down without a word, staring at her. Suddenly he said, 'Is something wrong?'

'I...' She didn't have the courage to tell him directly, so she decided to try and let him down gently. 'I think we ought to postpone the wedding.'

'Postpone it!' He stared at her, his eyes shocked. 'For how long?'

'Indefinitely.'

His face slowly drained of all colour.

'When I met you,' Alicia said quickly, 'I thought I was ready to marry. I liked you, enjoyed your company, and knew you would fit into my life very easily.'

'Isn't that perfect?' he asked hoarsely.

'No, David,' she said thickly, deeply ashamed. 'It's manufactured. Like the rest of my personal life. It's——' she said unsteadily, and groped for his hand. 'David, I've made a terrible mess of my life. I don't know how, and I don't know why. But something is deeply wrong, and I've got to try and find out what it is.'

He stared at her, his eyes fierce with pain. 'You're saying I'm what's wrong?'

'David, I'm simply saying we both need a little time to think about it. Marriage is more than a big step. And much, much more than a strategic career move. It's a question of who you really are, and how you really want to live.'

'I've never seen you like this,' he said, staring. 'So serious, so emotional. Do you know we've never discussed our relationship before? I always assumed you saw it as I did. I ... guess I was kidding myself.'

'Well,' she looked away, her eyes darkening, 'I guess I was kidding myself too. But we came here for a romantic weekend and I find myself unable to give it to you.'

'This is it, then?' he asked thickly. 'Our engagement is—broken?'

'Only if you want it to be,' she said gently, lifting dark brows. 'I'm prepared to let it stand if you are.'

He seemed to breathe a sigh of relief. 'I want to keep it as it is. Maybe something's just got to you here in Paris, Alicia. Maybe once we're back in London you'll see things differently.'

'OK,' she said, nodding her dark head, but she knew exactly what had 'got' to her, and she knew the damage was irreversible. Jean-Marc Brissac had forced her to face the mirror of truth, and she had been compelled to look. That she wanted to scream and cry over what she saw was irrelevant. The damage was done and there was no way back.

CHAPTER FOUR

NEXT morning the telephone woke Alicia at seven-thirty. Eyes flashing open, she rolled over in the luxurious bed, groping for the receiver. As she picked it up with her left hand she saw her engagement ring and winced.

'Hello...?' she said huskily, eyes closing.

'You left the party at ten o'clock,' a dark, powerful male voice said curtly, shocking her into sitting up, her heart missing a beat, 'and came back to the Ritz at three in the morning! Where were you?'

Alicia found herself breathing erratically. 'That's none of your business!'

'It is if I want it to be,' he said softly, a threat implicit in his lazy voice. 'Or have you forgotten how much I enjoy exerting my will over you?'

She just sat there, her black hair tousled around bare shoulders, heart thudding, her white silk nightdress irresistibly feminine suddenly as she stared into space with excited anger in her dark, Latin eyes.

'Now,' Jean-Marc Brissac said under his breath, 'I want you to come to my room and have breakfast with me. We can talk about this——'

'No,' she said tightly, 'I haven't even got out of bed yet. Nor do I intend to for at least another hour. Goodbye.' Slamming the receiver down, she stared at it for a long moment, her pulses racing.

How did he manage to have this effect on her? It was like adrenalin invading her bloodstream, just to hear his voice.

Suddenly, she knew she was wide awake and had no hope of getting back to sleep. Picking up the phone, she rang room service and ordered breakfast. Then she got out of bed, and walked barefoot to the bathroom, the nightdress like a floor-length white silk camisole, skimming her slender body with elegant sensuality.

As she finished brushing her teeth, there was a peremptory knock on her door. Room service at the Ritz is better than ever, she thought with a lift of her brows, and went to the door to answer the knock.

With a gasp, she saw Jean-Marc Brissac's hard grey eyes and tried to slam the door in his face. He pushed it open, strode in, slammed it behind him.

'Oh, God...' Alicia backed shakily, her heart hammering. 'What do you think you're doing? Get out..!'

'You said you were still in bed,' he told her flatly. 'What did you expect me to do—sit alone in my suite imagining what you looked like? Of course I came straight here. I couldn't do anything else.'

'Get out!' she repeated jerkily.

'I can't!' he said with a grim smile, staring at her, his grey eyes moving restlessly, intently over her body. 'I had to see you first thing in the morning. I knew you'd look sensational, but, my God, I didn't think you'd knock me breathless!'

'You can't be breathless,' she said weakly, running an unsteady hand through her long dark tousled hair. 'You're not the type!'

'I know! That's what bothers me!' he said under his breath, and came slowly towards her, a darkness in his eyes that almost terrified her.

'Don't come near me!' she whispered, her eyes staring as she backed. 'I'll scream . . . !'

'Go ahead!' he said, his face darkly flushed.

'No . . .' Her hands fluttered weakly to his broad shoulders, her mouth going dry.

'Yes!' he said thickly, and scooped her into his powerful arms, his mouth coming down hard on hers. Alicia moaned, helpless to resist, her hands thrusting at once into his hair as she went dizzy, her mouth opening beneath his.

He made a harsh sound of excitement under his breath, picked her up in his arms, and strode to the bedroom, kicking open the door, his eyes blazing with a dark, ruthless intent that made her whole body burn.

He threw her on the bed. She stared up at him, overwhelmed by the stark masculinity of him as he looked down at her, his grey eyes flickering over her supine, helpless body and the way she was breathing, so hoarsely and so wildly, her breasts rising and falling in that acute tense silence.

Then he joined her on the bed, and she gave a hoarse cry as his strong head lowered and he began to kiss her, forcing her mouth open with a hot, insistent pressure that she immediately responded to, helpless with the fierce desire that seemed to crash in through barriers that could not withstand the torrent any longer.

She was kissing him back, dazed and drowning in a sea of pleasure, her eyes closed as they exchanged kisses endlessly, exploringly, their hands running unconsciously over each other's throats, Alicia's fingers pushing into his thick dark hair as she abandoned herself to him, arching in sweet response to his powerful brand of lovemaking.

His hands were stroking down her body, stroking up again, and suddenly they were closing over her breasts, making her melt and shiver all at the same time, her nipples so hard that they almost stung with sexual excitement as he stroked down the bodice of her loose satin nightdress to expose them. He gave a rough sound of pleasure, and Alicia's fingers shook in his hair as he lowered his darkly flushed face to slide his hot mouth over her bare breast.

Her hoarse cry of abandoned desire as her nipple slid into his mouth made him groan thickly, his breathing ragged as he raised his head, eyes black with desire, and a second later his mouth closed over hers again, forcing the heat higher as he kissed her even more deeply, his strong fingers stroking down to her thighs, gently pulling the satin nightdress up, up, up until her slim thighs were bared to his fingers.

He was shrugging out of his grey jacket, throwing it to the floor, his breathing hoarse as he loosened his silk tie, eyes glittering with fever, his heartbeat crashing in his powerful chest.

When he came back to her, his mouth closed over hers again, and this time Alicia was swept away on a deep tide of erotic sensation, moaning thickly as she felt his hard thigh slide between hers and his hands gently tug the bodice of her satin nightdress down to the waist.

They did not hear the knock at the outside door. They were lost in the powerful sea of mutual desire, their eyes closed and their mouths hungry for each other, their hands moving restlessly, exploringly over each other's bare torsos.

Footsteps approached the open bedroom door. The rattle of a tea-trolley clunking into the suite living-room was a distant nuisance. But the knock on the bedroom door itself was loud and confident enough to make them blink, staring at each other dazedly in their hot bed of sin.

As Jean-Marc Brissac turned his head blindly to stare over one powerful bare shoulder, Alicia stared dazedly too, and what she saw made her go white and rigid.

David stood in the doorway, staring in blank shock, his blue eyes stretched wide with horrified understanding.

The silence was appalling. Behind him, the waiter was setting out the breakfast she had ordered on the linen-covered trolley, arranging silver and cups, and the awful mundane rattle made Alicia feel sick.

David just turned round and walked out of the room. The slam of the door as he left made Alicia wince.

'David...!' she whispered, closing her eyes to blot out the truth of what he had seen: what she had done.

'He had to find out sooner or later, Alicia,' Jean-Marc said deeply, watching her face. 'This isn't the first time. It will not be the last.'

'Yes, it will!' Bitterly, her eyes flashed back open. 'Because I hate you for what you've just done!'

'For what *I've* just done?' he asked grimly.

Hot colour flooded her face. 'You forced your way in this room and forced yourself on me, just as you have continually over the last twenty-four hours!'

'That's a blatant lie and not worthy of you!' he said bitingly.

She closed her eyes at once, desperate to shut out those penetrating grey eyes and the ruthless face, aware of the truth she could not bring herself to admit, even though she lay here like this, her breasts still warm from his exciting caresses, his powerful hair-roughened chest exposed to her gaze, and the sweet flood of sensual pleasure still pulsing through her veins.

'He doesn't love you,' Jean-Marc said ruthlessly. 'He is in love with your persona—not your true self. He wants the famous beauty who wins awards and commands respect. Has he ever tried to reach the woman in you? To reach her and make her burn?'

'Shut up!' she said thickly, keeping her eyes shut. 'Just shut up!'

There was a silence, then his hand thrust into her tousled hair, tugging her head backwards, making her gasp, eyes opening to stare at him in acute awareness.

'The war is over!' Jean-Marc said thickly. 'You are mine! I could have taken you just now, and you must admit that. Lie to yourself and you will only strengthen the web of lies you're caught in!'

'What web of lies?' she asked hoarsely, shaking. 'I don't know what you're talking about!'

He smiled grimly and released her hair, his mouth hard. 'Do you not, *chérie*? Then why are you still engaged to a man you do not respect?'

'I do respect him!' she protested angrily.

'No.' He shook his dark head. 'He is not man enough for you and you know it. He wanders around after you, full of admiration and worship, and boasts to his friends of his fabulous bride-to-be. But he does not love you—and you do not love him. Your engagement is a sham. And who proposed it?'

Bitterly, she looked into his grey eyes and said nothing.

'Did you propose to him?' Jean-Marc drawled with cool ruthlessness. 'I think not. Yet you accepted him. Why? Because you were too afraid to seek and find real love.'

'Shut up!' she whispered, hatred filling her.

'You tell me to shut up because I tell you things you cannot face,' he said in a hard voice. 'To find real love is to make yourself vulnerable. And that is your fatal flaw, Alicia. Vulnerability is the one part of you that you cannot reveal, yet it is the most vital if you are to fall in love.'

'I don't want to fall in love!' she said fiercely, almost squirming under the lethal accuracy of his words. 'It's a stupid, pointless waste of energy!'

'I agree,' he drawled sardonically. 'But I do not offer you love.'

'No, I know exactly what you're offering me!' she spat.

'And you respond excitingly to my demands,' he said with sardonic mockery.

Alicia trembled with rage, hot colour sweeping her face. 'Get out! I never want to see your face again!'

'No doubt,' he drawled, and slid off the bed, his magnificent chest making her go dry-mouthed with treacherous desire as she stared at him through dark Latin eyes, and felt his burning gaze rest on her naked breasts, noting the erect pink swell of her nipples.

Angrily, she tugged the nightdress up to cover herself, feeling appalled by her sense of vulnerability, her hand shaking as she watched him dress, shrugging his white shirt on, buttoning it up with strong fingers, never taking his heavy-lidded grey gaze from her for a second.

'I will tell Dominique that you agree to take the job,' Jean-Marc said with insolent self-assurance, knotting his silk tie. 'She will be delighted.'

'Don't tell her anything of the sort!' she said with thick hatred. 'I'd rather die than ever meet you again!'

'How you cut your nose off,' he drawled, bending to kiss her flushed face, 'to spite your beautiful face!'

Angrily, she jerked away from him, but his hard mouth left its burning imprint on her high slanting cheekbones. He picked up his jacket and slung it over one broad shoulder with a lazy arrogance she found devastatingly exciting.

'See you at the château!' he drawled, strolling to the bedroom door, a hard smile of triumph on his mouth, and blew her a kiss with one strong hand.

Was it possible, she wondered, to hate someone as violently as she hated Jean-Marc Brissac? Her engagement was now in ruins. Torn to shreds in twenty-four hours by that ruthless swine, and he was triumphant about it.

She groaned at the thought of David, what she would say to him, how she would ever be able to face him, but she knew she had to. They still had another day left in Paris, and her heart ached for him at the realisation that the romantic weekend they had planned should have turned out like this.

Taking a quick shower, she ignored her breakfast, feeling sick at the sight of it and the vivid memories it conjured up. She didn't know how she was going to explain this to David or how she was going to save his male pride.

Certainly, she had to see him quickly. David had his self-respect, and that was what she would have to protect in the way she approached her explanation.

Dressing, she found herself choosing a very severe business dress in navy blue that fitted her slender shape perfectly, and had a stark elegance that echoed the severity of the chignon she ruthlessly pulled her black hair into.

It was almost an obstinate refusal to admit the changes in her, and she knew it. Out of the old, classical and severe image stared a pair of dark gypsy eyes flashing with wild emotion, and a pair of red lips bruised with passion from Jean-Marc's hot kisses.

Angrily, she pushed the thoughts from her mind, and went along the corridor to David's room. He wasn't there. After knocking persistently, she was forced to take the lift downstairs, to find he had left his key at Reception and checked out.

*   *   *

When she arrived back in London, she took a taxi straight to her Chelsea house. The house was silent, of course, because she lived alone. As she opened the door she saw the handwritten letter on the doormat and her heart sank as she recognised David's writing. He said some terrible things, and she winced at each cutting sentence. How could she blame him? It hurt, though, and made her feel colossal guilt.

Next day, she was discussing the evening gowns of the winter collection with her redheaded assistant, Deb. Standing in her office, leafing through big, bold design drawings, she paused at the scarlet taffeta ballgown when the door burst open and her niece Lindy rushed in, dark hair flying wildly, eyes filled with hurt accusation.

'Is it true?' Lindy demanded hoarsely, her sweet young face suffused with hot colour. 'Are you Jean-Marc's latest mistress?'

Every muscle in her body stiffened. 'You can go, Deb!' she told her assistant.

Lindy was breathing erratically, the powder-blue dress emphasising her youth. Deb moved reluctantly from the office.

'Lindy, I——' Alicia began gently.

'You're going to deny it, aren't you?' Lindy said bitterly. 'David said you would.'

'David!' Alicia put a hand to her horrified mouth, wincing, saying aloud in an unguarded whisper, 'I can't believe it was he who told you!'

'Well, it wouldn't be Jean-Marc!' Lindy was shaking. 'He'd rather die than ever contact *me* again! Besides—he doesn't kiss and tell! He leaves that to his mistresses! Welcome to the ranks, Alicia, you——'

'Please . . . !' Alicia winced as she moved towards her young niece protectively. 'Darling, don't upset yourself like this! I can't bear to see you so——'

'Then why did you do it?' she said hoarsely. 'Why, Alicia . . . how could you?'

Alicia said thickly, 'It wasn't deliberate. Please believe me.'

'David said you were in bed together!'

'We were on the bed,' Alicia whispered, appalled by the way it sounded. 'That's not the same thing.'

Lindy stared, hatred in her eyes. 'You bitch!'

Alicia whitened, taken aback by the adult facing her, and felt the strings that had tied her to her niece being severed as though hacked with a machete.

'You wanted to prove you could get him!' Lindy said shakingly. 'He was an achievement for you, wasn't he? Just like all the other achievements you've notched up over the years!'

'Please don't say any more,' Alicia said hoarsely. 'Not because of Jean-Marc Brissac, Lindy! Don't let him come between us like this!'

'It's too late!' Lindy shook herself free, her voice hard with jealous pain. 'He already has, and that's your doing, Alicia. You've finally overreached yourself, haven't you? What a towering achievement! My clever aunt Alicia has caught the Last of the Great French Lovers!'

'He's only a man!' Alicia said fiercely. 'Stop using that stupid title!'

'But you wanted him, didn't you? And you got him! Title and all!' She looked her up and down with blazing contempt. 'I hope you're proud of yourself!'

Turning on her heel, she walked out of the room, slamming the door behind her. Alicia stood in white-faced agony for a moment, then turned and went to the desk, picked up the receiver and rang her sister.

'I have to speak to you,' she broke out as soon as Susannah answered the phone. 'Is there any chance I could come over for lunch today?'

'Well!' Susannah drawled with wry amusement. 'My baby sister taking time off work! Isn't that sacrilegious?'

'This is different,' Alicia said thickly, 'I'll be there at one.'

Susannah lived in a lovely little house in Richmond. The sun shone down over the leafy street, the row of suburban houses warm with family atmosphere.

Alicia parked her red Jaguar XJS convertible in the driveway and walked up the path, smart as paint in her bright red mini-skirt suit, her black hair pulled back severely.

'Hello, love.' Susannah answered the door, looking as she always did: dark and plump and pretty. With a flowered dress and white Peter Pan collar, she exuded warmth. When they were settled at the pine table with quiche and salad, Alicia briefly outlined Lindy's visit to the office.

'David was here for dinner last night,' Susannah told her calmly. 'He told us everything. I knew it was deliberate when I saw Lindy's face.'

'I can't believe David would do it!' Alicia was appalled. 'To betray me like this...'

'He obviously wanted to put a rocket under your perfect life.'

She blinked dark lashes. 'Perfect . . . ?'

Susannah studied her wryly. 'It's always seemed perfect. Although, I must admit, I did begin to wonder when you got engaged to David. He didn't seem to fit.'

'Didn't he?' Alicia was shocked by her words.

'No. He used to boast about you a lot down at the pub. I didn't like that. It didn't seem like love to me.'

Alicia paled, pushing her uneaten quiche away.

'I knew you wouldn't be happy with him, love.' Susannah put a hand over hers. 'He couldn't believe his luck when you agreed to a date. And when you agreed to marry him I began to worry. He would eventually have resented everything about you that makes you you.'

Alicia looked away, unable to take it in.

'So what about Jean-Marc Brissac?' Susannah asked suddenly. 'Where does he fit into all this?'

Mouth tightening, she said thickly, 'He's the catalyst! He wants me, Susannah. I don't know why, but he made a determined bid to get me, and he succeeded for a few devastating moments in Paris.' Her eyes flashed with bitterness. 'That's why poor Lindy has been hurt . . .'

'She'll get over it,' Susannah said with a fond smile. 'She's only seventeen. She doesn't know who she is yet. How can she know who she loves?'

'But if you could have heard the things she said . . .' Alicia broke out hoarsely.

'You should hear what she says to me!' Susannah laughed. 'My God, that girl is the absolute epitome of the rebellious teenager!'

Alicia stared, dark brows rising. 'You mean she might forgive me?'

'Of course she'll forgive you!' Susannah said, astonished. 'She adores you! And what she felt for that gorgeous Frenchman was just infatuation.'

'She said he made a pass at her!'

'Oh, don't be ridiculous, Alicia. You ought to have more sense. You're talking about Jean-Marc Brissac, the Last of the Great French Lovers. Not some third-rate Casanova from Clapham. He's a rich, powerful, very sexy man,' Susannah said flatly. 'If he wants you, Alicia, I can see exactly why. But Lindy was just his goddaughter's teenage schoolfriend. Why on earth would he bother to make a pass at her?'

'For the same reason he made a pass at me,' she said icily, hauteur seeping into her face. 'He was bored!'

Susannah laughed. 'Are you really Alicia Holt?'

Her eyes darted uncertainly over her sister's face.

'Go and look in the mirror,' Susannah said coolly. 'You'll see why he wants you.'

'My looks?' Alicia said scornfully. 'Really! I don't want a——'

'I didn't mean a real mirror, Alicia.' Her sister arched her dark brows with irony, and Alicia just stared at her in silence.

When she got home that night, she studied David's unpleasant letter, and wondered what she should do. If she contacted him to try and explain he might turn even nastier than he had done already.

But her sense of honour demanded that she speak to him, explain, and return the engagement ring personally.

The doorbell rang as she was making herself low-calorie soup, and she tensed, staring from her small, neat kitchen to the front door. If it was David, she might have an unpleasant scene on her hands. Making a face, she turned off the heat below the soup, and walked to the door.

'Miss Holt?' A man in black motorbike helmet and leathers stood before her.

'Yes?'

'Courier delivery from Paris for you,' he said, holding out a large package, and then a slip of paper. 'Sign here.'

Alicia opened the package in the kitchen a minute later. A stunning black silk nightdress nestling in folds of tissue paper made her catch her breath. Picking up the envelope that was also there, she tore it open with shaking hands.

'You might need this,' Jean-Marc Brissac had written in bold black strokes, 'when you arrive at my château.'

Furious, she tore the nightdress from the box, tempted to stamp on it in her rage. Then she saw the air ticket flutter to the floor along with a detailed timetable specifying when she should arrive in Paris, how she would be taken to the château in a chauffeur-driven limousine, and how long she would have to stay.

He can go to hell! she thought, seething inside.

The doorbell rang again, and she strode over to it, eyes blazing with temper, pulled it open and caught her breath with a shock as she saw David standing there.

'Hi, beautiful!' he drawled with an unpleasant smile. 'I've come for a chat.'

She paled, and stepped back with a cold nod, allowing him to step over the threshold. As she closed the door, she knew he hated her, and that it was probably what he had really felt all along.

'Thought we might have——' he began, and broke off. 'What's this?' Suddenly, he was walking to the kitchen door, picking up the black nightdress from the floor and the note Jean-Marc Brissac had sent.

'Put that down!' Alicia rushed to stop him.

'My God!' David screwed up the note, blue eyes incredulous as he turned on her. 'You really have dropped me for him, haven't you?'

'David, that note is——'

'All too revealing!' he said tightly. 'I knew you'd never marry me! I knew it! I thought I'd fallen in a pot of jam when you accepted a date with me! My friends said if I ended up marrying you I'd be set up for life, and I would have been, wouldn't I? If it hadn't been for that bastard Brissac!'

Alicia reeled under the impact of his blunt confession. 'You're not saying——'

'That I only wanted you for your money?' His mouth twisted and his blue eyes flicked over her slender curves with angry desire. 'No, love! I wanted a lot more than that! But Brissac got it instead of me, didn't he?'

'David,' she said shakily, 'you mustn't say these things. Not in anger. You're making me think you never even liked me, and I——'

'Can't bear to face it?' He nodded. 'I knew that, too. Just as I knew you would never go to bed with me outside marriage. That's why I was so patient with you. Didn't you ever ask yourself why?'

Alicia closed her eyes momentarily, the enormity of what he was saying hitting her like a tidal wave of truths she had always suspected and was now being forced to face.

There was a sudden acute silence.

'Oh, God,' David's voice said roughly, 'I've hurt you.'

She looked up into his face, her eyes bleak, dark coals.

He winced. 'I didn't mean to do that.'

Alicia drew a deep breath. 'You should have thought about that before you went around hacking me up into tiny pieces, David. Not only to my face—but to my family, as well.' Her brows lifted. 'You didn't just hurt me. You hurt Lindy, too, and you definitely didn't need to do that.'

He had the good grace to redden, shame evident in his lowered eyes.

Alicia slowly removed the engagement ring from her finger. 'I can see that you've acted out of hurt and anger, David. I can see that you're ashamed of what you've done.' Holding out the ring, she said in a low voice, 'But more than anything, I can see that you do not love me and never did.'

He took the ring, turning it over with a grimace. 'I went too far, didn't I?'

'Yes, David,' she said tightly. 'You went much too far. And now, I really think you've come to the end of the line.'

He flicked a look of grim acceptance at her, nodded, and left the house without another word. Alicia stood listening to the silence for a long time.

Tears welled up in her eyes. What a horrible mess.

The telephone rang.

Wiping tears away with quick fingers, she walked to it and picked up the elegant receiver, trying to sound cool and collected, but aware that her voice was husky and vulnerable.

'Alicia?' The powerful male voice picked up her mood instantly. 'What's wrong?'

Her pulses raced with a blend of anger and excitement at the sound of his voice. 'What do you want?'

'I called to find out if you had received my gift,' Jean-Marc Brissac said flatly. 'But I can see something else has got to you instead. Or should I say someone? David Balham has——'

'I don't know what you're talking about!' she snapped, her voice hoarse, reacting like a scalded cat to his astute guess and the concern behind it.

'He's been there!' Jean-Marc bit out thickly. 'My God—what did he do?'

'Nothing!' she said bitterly, hating him. 'But you'll be pleased to hear my engagement is in ruins, and it's all thanks to you!'

'You're right,' he said deeply. 'I am pleased. But I want you to promise me never to see him again, Alicia.'

'Go to hell!' she said thickly, and slammed down the telephone.

It rang again almost instantly.

'Want me to fly over and extract that promise from you by force?' his voice sniped at her.

She drew a ragged breath. 'What business is it of yours? Why won't you leave me alone?'

'Because I want you, Alicia,' his hard voice said. 'And I *will* have you.'

Her mouth went dry and she clutched the receiver in silence, breathing erratically, picturing those steel-grey eyes and the hard mouth and what he would do if she argued.

'We understand each other,' he said under his breath when she remained silent. 'I will come and get you if you aren't on that plane. Now stop arguing with me. I'll see you on Friday.'

The line went dead in her hands and she drew a ragged breath, replaced the receiver and cursed him as she shook with rage. He meant it. If she didn't arrive at his château on Friday night, he would fly over and cause even more chaos in her life than he had already.

He had caused the ruin of her engagement and the appalling aftermath. He had caused all of it, from start to finish. All right, so she should never have agreed to marry a man like David. But it had not had to end so bitterly, and Jean-Marc Brissac was directly responsible for it.

Alicia thought of her sweet, vulnerable niece. Jean-Marc had broken Lindy's heart without compunction. Everyone appeared to believe Lindy was making it up, but Alicia had been under attack from the man herself, and she knew to her cost exactly how powerful his sexual impact could be. If she was reduced to a shaking, helpless wreck by the touch of those hard hands and that demanding mouth, how had poor little Lindy felt?

I'll go to France, she thought angrily, and when I get there I'll give Jean-Marc Brissac a taste of his own medicine. He wants me, he says. Well, he will find out that he can't have me! Not with all the stark insistence of his lovemaking! I'll resist him if I have to fight him to the death!

I'm going to teach that arrogant swine a lesson he'll never forget!

CHAPTER FIVE

ALICIA left her offices early on Friday and went home to change and pack a small overnight bag. She would not be staying long in France. Just long enough to slap Jean-Marc Brissac's insolent face and prove to him that here was one woman who found him resistible.

She dressed with care in her favourite red wool dress, sleek-fitting and sexy, her hair pulled back and her dark eyes smouldering with temper. As she left the house, she felt a surge of adrenalin, stopped a taxi and sank back, enjoying the rage as it built in her veins. The private jet waited on the tarmac, glittering red and powerful. But she refused to feel affected by the symbols of his power, and settled back to be waited on hand and foot by the team of stewardesses who had no other passengers but her.

Touchdown in Paris brought back memories. She smiled savagely. Jean-Marc Brissac had a come-uppance due him, and she would deliver it, even if it killed her. The limousine that met her was another symbol of power and wealth. Alicia rode in the luxurious rear, flicking coolly through French *Vogue*, barely seeing the clothes, her mind revolving continually on how he would look when his seduction technique failed and Alicia slapped his hard, handsome face with a mocking laugh.

When the limousine reached Château Brissac, however, Alicia felt her courage fade at this, the last and most breathtaking of all the symbols of power. Those endless bleached-stone walls, lead turrets, archways—the sheer size of the medieval château and grounds were awe-inspiring.

But she had come this far, and she refused to back down now. Stepping coolly from the limousine, she walked up to the towering arched front doors, which were open, and walked into the fifty-foot-high hallway.

A silver-haired butler in black uniform approached her. 'Bonsoir, Mademoiselle Holt. Monsieur Brissac has instructed that you be shown to your bedroom straight away. Please follow me. The chauffeur will bring your bags.'

Surprised, Alicia followed him up the sweeping stone staircase. She had expected to see Jean-Marc Brissac immediately. A quiver of disappointment ran through her. Angrily, she suppressed it.

Refusing to be impressed by the stately grandeur of the château, she gave the butler a cool nod of polite thanks when he showed her into her bedroom.

'I hope you will find everything to your satisfaction,' he said with a smile, and withdrew.

Alicia raged inwardly at the way she was being treated. This bedroom was fit for Catherine de Medici, with a four-poster bed, antique furniture and deep pile rugs on the polished floor, but she knew she was being treated as a conquered trophy by Jean-Marc Brissac.

Unpacking her small overnight case, she saw the black nightdress he had sent her and smiled savagely. She would most certainly not be wearing this: she would return it with cold indifference.

The knock at her door made her stiffen, turning. *'Entrez!'* she called sharply, and watched it open to admit Jean-Marc Brissac himself.

He was devastating in a black business suit, his silk tie loosened, his shirt unbuttoned at the throat, making his sex appeal even more heart-stopping.

Just the sight of him made fierce rage flood her veins.

'You came, then,' he said with a gleam of triumph in his grey eyes.

Inflamed, she said, 'I have a business to run! I don't want to make an enemy of you, Monsieur Brissac! You left me little choice!'

He laughed softly. 'That's not why you came,' he said deeply, and walked with lazy arrogance towards her.

She lifted her head, haughty anger in her eyes. 'You're right. I came because I was angry enough to want to see you personally and——'

'Not indifferent, then?' He was towering over her, the nearness of him sending prickles of awareness all over her skin. 'I'm glad to hear it. And you look well, Alicia. Even more beautiful than I remembered.'

'Thank you,' she said insultingly. 'I can't reply in kind. You're not my type.'

'And you hate it when I kiss you.'

'Yes!' she flamed. 'I hate it!'

His gaze slid to the four-poster bed beside them. 'You brought the nightdress, though?'

Hot colour flooded her face. 'Only to tell you what you can do with it!'

'I know exactly what to do with it!' he drawled, insolence in his grey eyes. 'That's why I——'

Alicia snatched up the black scrap of silk and lace suddenly, and tore it straight down the middle, her dark eyes blazing. The material ripped easily. With a burst of rage, she threw it at his feet, her face filled with fierce challenge.

He looked down at it. 'Yes. That was more or less what I had in mind.'

'Very funny!' Alicia was trembling.

'Even funnier,' he said softly, flicking his grey gaze back to hers, 'if you now have to sleep without it.'

'I brought my own,' she said with a great deal of satisfaction. 'And I only intend to stay in this wretched place for one night, so it won't hurt me an inch!'

'One night?' He frowned. 'My arrangements specified two.'

'Those are formal business arrangements that go with the job,' she said icily. 'And as I don't intend to take the job, they are irrelevant.'

His smile mocked her. 'You came all this way just to tell me you don't want the job? Shame on you, Alicia. That's time-wasting and unworthy of you.'

'As I said—I can't offend you, Monsieur Brissac.' She folded her arms, her face icily haughty. 'I therefore came in person to refuse.'

'You don't want to offend me, and yet you came here to insult me?' He was laughing at her, secret mockery in his eyes. 'Alicia! You'll go out of business!'

'Oh, don't twist my words!' she said huskily, looking away, aware that he was going to be able to make a fool of her if she didn't change tactics pretty fast.

'Is that really what you came to refuse, Alicia?' he asked with a cool shrewdness that infuriated her. 'The job?'

'What else?' she challenged at once.

'What else indeed?' he murmured, and one strong hand took hers, lifting it to inspect the ringless finger, satisfaction in his grey eyes. 'Free, then?'

'I told you.' Angrily, she pulled her hand from his. 'My engagement is in ruins. I'm sure you're delighted.'

He studied her face. 'Was it very unpleasant, Alicia?'

'No, just mildly devastating!' she said bitterly.

'Are you talking about the reactions of your friends? Or was it David who devastated you?'

'Do you really care?' she asked, eyes scornful. 'It wouldn't have happened if you hadn't engineered it. Thanks to you, I was almost hacked to pieces and turned into pâté where my family are concerned.'

His eyes narrowed. 'What do you mean—hacked to pieces?'

She met his gaze with bitterness. 'David went to see my sister. She's the only surviving member of my family. Her daughter is——' She broke off, not wanting to discuss Lindy with him, because it could cause far more damage than had already been done to her niece.

'Yes? Her daughter is?'

'Nothing.' Alicia lowered her gaze angrily, staring at the dark silk tie at eye level, his broad, hard-muscled chest disturbingly attractive, particularly as that tie was loose and she could see the beginnings of dark hairs where the shirt collar was unbuttoned twice.

There was a contemplative silence.

Jean-Marc Brissac drawled softly, 'Do you know, Alicia . . . sometimes I think you keep things from me?'

Her gaze shot to his face.

'I know who your sister's daughter must be,' he said deeply. 'Lindy Sullivan. And I know what you must be thinking about——'

'I don't wish to discuss it,' she cut in icily, protective towards Lindy, knowing it would be horribly unfair if she discussed her with Jean-Marc Brissac when she wasn't here to defend herself.

'She told you about her stay here at the château,' Jean-Marc said. 'And you told David.'

Alicia remained utterly silent, hating him.

'That's what he used when he got home,' Jean-Marc said. 'He wanted revenge on you because he found you in my arms.' He studied her, his hard mouth angry. 'The best revenge was to turn your niece against you. David knew exactly where to stick the knife, didn't he?'

'Does that satisfy you, Jean-Marc?' she asked thickly. 'Does that make you feel good?'

'I'm right, then.' His eyes narrowed. 'How great was the damage, Alicia? Is it serious? Can I do anything to help?'

She looked at him, her dark eyes bitter, and said under her breath, 'I think you've done quite enough, Monsieur Brissac. Don't you?'

'Tell me, Alicia.' He wasn't going to let it go until he knew what had happened, and his strong hands pressed hers as he scrutinised her face. 'What happened? Lindy came to see you?' He caught the involuntary gasp she gave as he said that, and his eyes narrowed as he went on. 'At work, I take it, where it would shock you, catch you off guard and cause the maximum impact?'

She was shocked by his accuracy. That mind missed nothing. 'Lindy burst in while I was in the middle of a design discussion,' she heard herself say huskily. 'She was hysterical. She said some terrible things...'

He nodded, mouth grim. 'And that hurt more than the break-up with David.'

The astuteness of his remark took her breath away, made her stare at him with ill-concealed shock, and then the tide of colour rose in her cheeks.

'So clever, Jean-Marc!' she said bitterly. 'Do you want to make me despise myself?'

'For being afraid to fall in love?' He gave an ironic laugh. 'I've made a life's work of it.'

'I didn't know I was afraid,' she said, her face paling as she looked away, 'I thought I loved David. I intended to marry him. I just...hadn't really thought about whether or not we were suited.'

'And now you know he was always just a friend,' he said deeply.

Alicia hesitated, then gave a stiff nod, her face averted.

He was silent for a moment, then bent his dark head and kissed her high slanting cheekbone. Before she could react, her heart leaping, he had stepped away, watching her with a hard smile on his mouth, saying, 'I have to go back downstairs now. Attend to my guests. You will, of course, join us as soon as you can.'

'Guests?' She stiffened involuntarily. 'What guests? You didn't mention about——'

'Dominique is here with her young man,' he said, dark brows lifting. 'And my closest friend—Pierre Dusort—is also here. A small, casual gathering of friends. Nothing more. You need not feel pressurised.'

'I don't feel pressurised,' she said with cool hauteur, lifting her dark brows and folding her arms. 'I simply don't see why you've brought me here.'

'To design Dominique's wedding,' he murmured, mouth indenting with humour. 'A subject we shall discuss when you come downstairs.'

'It's pointless,' she said angrily. 'I won't be taking the job. I shouldn't have come here, I can't stay, I'll be leaving in the morning!'

'No,' he said, sliding his grey eyes to her mouth and making her heart skip beats. 'You won't be leaving until this is settled.' He turned and strode with cool authority to the door, opening it, his strong hand familiar with the carved bronze door-handle and every inch of breathtaking grandeur in this magnificent château.

Alicia burnt to ask him what he meant about leaving when this was settled. But of course she knew exactly what he meant. And her body was pulsing with deep response as he closed the door behind him, that implicit yet veiled sexual threat hanging in the air.

Quickly, she picked up the torn black silk night-dress. She had made a fool of herself by doing that, and Jean-Marc's sardonic smile of mockery as he watched her had made her want to kill him.

When she went downstairs, she felt lost in the vast hallway, and even more lost when she found herself with a choice of so many doors.

'This way, *mademoiselle*.' The butler appeared from nowhere, startling her, and she murmured polite thanks in French as she followed him to the drawing-room.

Conversation halted as she entered. Jean-Marc Brissac stood by the elegant carved wood fireplace, hands thrust in black trouser pockets, his stance one of lazy masculine authority.

Alicia's dark gaze swung rapidly from face to face. Two teenagers were sprawled on the sofa, elegant and fresh-faced. An attractive man in his late thirties sat in an armchair, smiling at her.

'Alicia,' Jean-Marc strolled coolly towards her, speaking in a French drawl, 'won't you come in? I'd like to present you to my oldest friend: Pierre Dusort.'

He guided her, one possessive hand at the small of her back, over to the distinguished man with dark hair who was rising to his feet.

'*Enchanté, mademoiselle*.' Pierre Dusort gallantly kissed her hand, his dark eyes warm. 'Jean-Marc told me you were beautiful. I see he did not exaggerate.'

Alicia flushed, shooting a cool look at Jean-Marc through her lashes. 'Thank you.' She gave Pierre a smile. 'I'm very pleased to meet you.'

Jean-Marc turned her, guided her to the teen-agers on the sofa. 'And my goddaughter, Dominique Dusort...'

'I'm very pleased to meet you,' Alicia said, smiling at the very beautiful young woman with long dark hair, dark eyes and a bright green silk dress on her slender body. 'Jean-Marc has told me so much about you.'

'Jean-Marc told you about me?' Dominique's dark eyes swivelled in teasing adoration to his hard face. 'What did he say? Tell, tell!'

'I said you were a spoilt brat!' Jean-Marc drawled with wry indulgence, continuing smoothly, 'And this young man is her fiancé, Olivier.'

'Enchanted.' Olivier's charm as he deftly kissed Alicia's hand was rather sweet, and she could see why young Dominique wanted to marry him.

Conversation began once she was settled in a deeply luxurious dark red antique chair. Alicia grappled with her French, flexing muscles as she forced herself to simply use the old trick of never translating, but instead just thinking in French, and by the time Jean-Marc had poured her a second glass of red wine, she was laughing at something Pierre Dusort had said and feeling half-French herself, speaking the language with ease, her accent superb.

'Are you hungry?' Jean-Marc had drawn his chair close to hers from the beginning, and leaned forward as the others talked, his deep voice intimate. 'I forgot to ask earlier, but——'

'I ate on the plane,' she said, her gaze meeting his with irony. 'Your stewardesses waited on me hand and foot.'

'Yes, they're good at that,' he drawled, with a sardonic smile. 'But you can take that look off your face, Alicia. I don't make a habit of seducing my staff—however attractive they are.'

'Does that mean you won't seduce me if I join the hallowed ranks?'

The grey eyes slid to her red mouth. 'Do you want my word of honour?'

'No,' she said. 'You have no honour.'

'Do I not?' he drawled, amused, then his eyes narrowed thoughtfully. 'Is this going to be a problem, Alicia? In taking this job? Dominique will be hurt if you refuse. I don't wish to spoil her wedding——'

Dominique suddenly called impishly in French, 'Hey! Stop seducing my designer, Jean-Marc! I need her brains unscrambled!'

Alicia went scarlet, mortified.

'Guard your tongue, Dominique!' Jean-Marc said at once, sharply.

Dominique flushed, mumbling, 'I'm sorry, Jean-Marc, I didn't mean——'

'Give your apologies to Mademoiselle Holt,' he said curtly.

The girl looked at Alicia and said huskily, 'I'm terribly sorry, Mademoiselle Holt. That was very rude of me. Please forgive me.' Her eyes pleaded with Alicia, and she felt deep compassion at once, realising how important Jean-Marc really was to this girl.

'That's quite all right, Dominique.' Alicia's French accent was husky, and she smiled at the girl reassuringly.

Jean-Marc was instantly charming as he said lazily to his goddaughter, 'Would you like to show Mademoiselle Holt the ballroom now? She'll need to see it if she is to take the job.'

'You show her, Jean-Marc!' Dominique's dark eyes lit up. 'I'll go and get my magazine cuttings, so she can see exactly what I have in mind.'

Alicia was taken along a myriad corridors, until finally they reached the ballroom, and she caught her breath at the sight of it, for it was vast, palatial, with a fifty-foot ceiling and a series of vast crystal chandeliers suspended high above her head.

'We expect around two hundred guests for the wedding itself,' Jean-Marc said briskly, striding in, hands thrust in black trouser pockets. 'Building to a final eight hundred for the evening reception.'

'That's a lot of guests!' Alicia said, brows lifting.

He shot her a cool smile. 'You see why it will need such close organisational direction.'

'Yes.' Alicia looked around the sweeping room. It was like a vast cavernous film set, mirrors gilding the endless walls, the floor a polished gold oak. 'But I'm not experienced enough. I'm a designer — not a party organiser.'

'Your design skills are all we require,' he said coolly. 'The ballroom must be completely re-vamped. But not permanently.' He gave a dry smile. 'I am not particularly fashion-conscious. I prefer classicism.' His grey eyes ran over her with sexual appraisal. 'It is one thing to admire female fashion such as your beautiful clothes, Alicia, but quite another to have my home turned into a trend-nightmare.'

'But you want this ballroom revamped?'

'I think "dressed" would be a better word,' he drawled, his deep voice echoing. 'Once the wedding is over—I want it exactly as it is now.' His eyes traced the room with deep love. 'Elegant and classical.'

Alicia smiled against her will, eyes flashing over his powerful body so impeccably classical in that black suit. She agreed with him. Fashion was one thing; total era-consciousness was another.

He turned his dark head, caught her admiring gaze, and moved towards her, a smile on his hard mouth. 'You will take the job?'

Alicia tried to freeze him with a haughty glance. 'You know I can't.'

He caught her by the waist with one powerful arm, pulling her against his hard body, ignoring her angry gasp. 'You must! I can't think of anyone else I would want to do it.'

'Then want,' she said angrily, struggling, 'must be your master!'

'No,' he said deeply, looking down into her flushed face. 'I will be *your* master, Alicia, and you will be my——'

'Mistress?' she asked bitterly, hands pushing at his broad shoulders. 'Yes, I know exactly what you have in mind, Monsieur Brissac! I don't know why I was stupid enough to come here!'

'But you did,' he said, and she met his grey gaze with acute awareness that, no matter what she said or did or how she tried to explain it to herself, he was right. She had come, and there was really nothing more to say.

Looking away, she said huskily, 'I don't know why I came! I was a fool!'

'You came because of what lies between us,' he said, watching her face.

'There's nothing between us!'

'Then why are you here?'

Stung, she lifted her head, dark eyes blazing, 'If you must know, I came to slap your face! I knew you'd try to seduce me, and I wanted to have the satisfaction of wiping that arrogant look off your face!'

He laughed under his breath, grey eyes flashing. 'How passionate you are, Alicia!'

'I'm not passionate! Well, I wasn't until I met you!' she snapped, hating him, and then realised what she had said with a gasp, 'Oh . . . !' and tried to hide her face in his powerful chest as her cheeks burned betraying scarlet.

'Alicia . . . !' Jean-Marc's laughter made her furious. He slid one strong hand below her chin and lifted her face to look at him, his grey eyes darkening as he said deeply, 'Don't fight me! You know it's useless.'

'You want to control me!' she said bitterly.

'No,' he said thickly, 'I want to stop you controlling yourself!'

Her eyes widened at his words; she was stricken, as though he had shot an arrow straight into her heart, bypassing all her defences, leaving her pierced to the core, her face white and her mouth quivering.

'And I will, Alicia.' He ran one finger over her high slanting cheekbone to her mouth. 'If I have to unleash all my power on you and force surrender, I will do it.'

'If that's really the way you feel,' she said bitterly, breaking out of his embrace, her eyes blazing,

'I can't stay here!' Stepping away from him, she said angrily, 'Thank you so much for the enlightening evening, Monsieur Brissac! But I'm afraid I must refuse the job, and your kind invitation to stay!' Her gaze raked him with contempt. 'I shall leave immediately and spend the night in a hotel!'

Turning on her heel, she strode to the door, furious with herself for being stupid enough to come here in the first place.

He followed her, caught her arm, his eyes intense. 'You can't go!'

She stared at him, astonished by the urgency in his voice.

'After all,' he drawled with a sudden lazy smile, 'you haven't slapped my face yet!'

Angrily, she raised her hand, eyes blazing at his mockery. He caught it easily, laughing under his breath.

'Another time, perhaps,' he murmured, 'when I deserve it a little more!'

'There won't be another time, Jean-Marc!' she said tightly. 'I'm leaving and I'm never coming back!'

'You're so tempestuous, darling!' he drawled.

Fury shot through her. 'Don't laugh at me!'

'I'm not!'

'And don't call me darling!' she said, face filled with hot colour.

'I'm trying to defuse your temper.' His voice hardened. 'You'll waste a rare opportunity, Alicia, if you walk out on this job. And you're more than capable of doing it.'

'So are plenty of other designers.'

'I want you,' he said flatly. 'I think you're exactly what we've been looking for. You're young enough to understand Dominique, but mature enough to keep a cool eye on her. She's inclined to go over the top, and that would spoil everything. Fashion becomes absurd unless there's a classical influence somewhere, and you have a strong streak of classicism, Alicia.'

She drew a level breath. 'You're not listening to me. I don't want the job. Not under these circumstances. Not if you're going to spend your time trying to seduce me.'

'But it will give you the chance to slap my face!' he drawled, grey eyes rakish. 'Surely that's an opportunity not to be wasted!'

She smiled against her will, lowering her lashes, her heart skipping a beat at the charm in his tough face.

'Take it,' he pressed, eyes narrowing calculatingly. 'It will break Dominique's heart if you don't. Surely you noticed she is wearing one of your own designs?'

Alicia's brows lifted. Yes, she had noticed. The green silk dress had been one of her favourites from this year's spring collection, and it suited Dominique's dark colouring superbly.

'All right,' she said flatly, eyes warring with him. 'I might *consider* taking the job. But only on one condition: you give me your word that you won't try to seduce me while I'm here.'

'You have it,' he said at once, and they both knew he was lying.

Alicia smiled sardonically. 'Jean-Marc, you'll have to mean it.'

He gave a grim smile. 'I do mean it—though God knows why. Take the job, Alicia. Give Dominique the wedding she wants.'

A deep sigh wrenched her. He was blackmailing her into it with Dominique, and it was a blackmail she found difficult to resist. The young girl was so charming, and so like Lindy, that Alicia could not help wanting to make the wedding a young girl's fairy-tale. Already, her designer's mind was flicking through the last year of fashion, picking out the possibilities of décor, food, wine, cars, flowers— and, of course, the dress itself, and all the brides- maids' dresses.

If the wedding was featured in all the magazines, she knew it would make her a household name. The dress she designed for Dominique would have to be the masterpiece of her career, and her heart beat with a strong excitement at the thought of it. What an exciting achievement . . .

Jean-Marc was watching the emotions playing across her face, and he said suddenly, 'Come back to the drawing-room. Let Dominique show you some of her ideas.'

Alicia shot him an angry look. 'You're pushing me into this!'

'I'll never push you anywhere you don't want to go,' he said softly, and opened the door.

With a feeling of excitement and foreboding, Alicia went back to the drawing-room and sat beside Dominique, listening to her enthusiastic chatter and studying her photographs and clippings. The young girl had a strong mind and a strong will. She also had a lot of very good ideas, and Alicia grew more interested in the whole idea than ever.

It would be like organising a whirlwind; but what a show-stopper!

As she sat with Dominique, talking, Jean-Marc refilled her wine glass, watching her with a cool smile. Deeply aware of him, she refused to glance in his direction, prickling.

He had promised not to try and seduce her while she was here, but, of course, she knew deep inside that that promise would prove impossible for him.

I'll just have to slap his face if he tries anything, Alicia thought coolly, and a smile touched her full mouth as she remembered him saying what a wasted opportunity it would be if she left without delivering that slap. Quite so! she thought.

'Well?' Jean-Marc asked close to midnight, when all the clippings were strewn all over the floor at Alicia's feet. 'Have you reached your decision?'

Feeling cornered, Alicia said flatly, 'Not yet.'

Dominique looked hurt. 'Oh, but...' She bit her lip, flicking her dark eyes to her godfather. '*Jean-Marc, tu m'as dit que——*'

'I didn't say I wouldn't take the job,' Alicia said with a smile to Dominique. 'I just need to think about it a little more. It's quite a task. I'd need to leave my assistant in charge of my London offices for at least a month.'

'I can fly you back at a moment's notice,' Jean-Marc said firmly.

'Oh...' Alicia frowned. 'I'd also need premises here to make up the dresses, do alterations...'

'That can be arranged,' he said coolly. 'Anything else?'

Her brows rose. 'A couture house in Paris to handle all the clothes.' She was trying to make it impossible, challenging him to refuse her very necessary demands. 'A top couture house, Jean-Marc! With skilled cutters, fitters——'

'I can arrange it,' he cut in coolly.

'Well—I'd need a rough estimate of how much you're prepared to spend. This is an expensive task, and it may be more than—— '

He named a sum that took her breath away.

'Oh . . .' She looked at his tough, clever face and lifted her brows. 'Well, it seems you've thought of everything, Jean-Marc!'

'Then you'll take the job?'

Her mouth compressed. She looked at the clippings on the floor. She looked at Dominique.

She was definitely cornered. It was a fantastic opportunity, a beautiful temporary workplace, a charming young bride and an astonishing sum of money, both as a salary and as a sum to play with.

She would have to be mad to refuse.

But she would also have to be mad to accept, because Jean-Marc Brissac wanted her, had made it clear that he would stop at nothing to get her, and the promise he had given her was irrelevant.

'Alicia?' Jean-Marc queried softly, grey eyes intent on her face.

'All right,' she said in a moment of folly, 'I'll take it.'

Dominique gave a cry of joy, clapped her hands and ran over to her fiancé Olivier to embrace him wildly. Pierre Dusort got to his feet, smiling, and came over to embrace Alicia.

'Thank you, *mademoiselle*!' he said, kissing her on each cheek. 'You've made my daughter very happy.'

Alicia murmured polite thanks, flushing as her eyes met Jean-Marc Brissac's, and she felt her heart stop with fear and excitement as she met the grey intensity of his eyes.

He had won.

But only for the moment, she told herself, lifting her dark head with cool hauteur and matching his gaze with equal determination.

CHAPTER SIX

NEXT morning, Alicia woke early. Her dream clung to her skin like love, and she closed her eyes as she remembered the way she had felt in her dream as Jean-Marc made slow, sensual love to her. Angrily, she pushed back the covers and got out of bed, padding to the bathroom in her white lace nightdress to shower his imagined touch from her skin.

When she came out, wrapped in a white towel, she found Jean-Marc lounging on her bed, leafing through her copy of French *Vogue*. He looked up as she appeared, and his face changed, stark sexual appraisal making her blood throb in hot response.

She took a step back, instinctively clutching the white bath-towel closer. 'What do you think you're doing in here?' Her voice was hoarse and shaking.

His lashes flickered, and he produced a casual smile. 'I came to wake you. Is there anything wrong with that?'

'Yes! This is my bedroom and you didn't come to wake me!' Alicia was deeply conscious of her defenceless nudity and his potent sexuality. 'You came to break your promise and——'

'I can assure you I didn't,' he said calmly, watching her.

Alicia tightened her lips, heart racing. Her eyes raced over him, suddenly noticing he wore black jodhpurs, long black riding boots, and a black sweater, his body more powerfully outlined than ever before, and quite intolerably sexy.

'As you see,' Jean-Marc drawled, 'I came to ask you to ride with me before breakfast.'

'I don't have any riding clothes,' she said stiffly.

'I brought you some,' he said, gesturing to the pile of dark clothes on the bed beside him. 'They're Dominique's. She's the same size as you—isn't she?'

Her lashes flickered. 'Possibly. What about the boots?'

'What size are your feet?' he asked coolly, adding, 'They look about average to me. But you're tall, aren't you? Although you have such fine bones...'

'Jean-Marc,' she said suddenly, her mouth dry, 'you must leave! I'm not wearing anything except a bath-towel, and you're making me very conscious of it!'

His eyes darkened, and he slowly got to his feet, walking towards her with a grim look of uncontrolled desire evident in the way he moved and the way he looked at her.

'Don't...!' she said fiercely, taking a step backwards, one hand up to defend herself. 'Please...!'

'It's OK,' he said softly, stopping in front of her with regret. 'I won't do anything. Well—I hope I won't!'

'You'll try to kiss me!' she accused, hot colour burning her face.

His smile was grim. 'I want to kiss you, Alicia. But I gave you my word, and I intend to keep it.'

For a full five seconds, they looked at each other in silence, and her heartbeat was so audible to her that she felt sure he must hear it because he stood so close and yet did not touch her.

'I'm glad you accepted the job,' Jean-Marc said suddenly, deeply. 'And I will try to keep my word.'

'Try?' she queried huskily, lifting her brows.

He smiled wryly. 'I'm only human, Alicia. I can't stop myself wanting you. And after all—a kiss is just a kiss. Even if it does send us both up in flames.'

He had switched back into French, and Alicia was beginning to get used to it, speaking and thinking half in each language as though born to it, her ear quick and her grasp of French strong.

'So...' he flicked that stark gaze of desire down to her bare shoulders, damp throat, the half-swell of her breasts '...will you ride with me?'

'I must leave today, Jean-Marc,' she said unsteadily, feeling her pulses race wildly as he looked at her. 'If I don't, you'll break your word, and then I must break mine.'

His gaze slid to her clean, fresh face, her wet hair. 'You'll refuse the job?'

'I'll have no choice,' she pointed out.

'Then I must keep my word,' he said softly, and moved away towards the door, taking her by surprise as he wrenched it open, looked at her over one broad shoulder and said, 'I'll be in the drawing-room, waiting for you. Don't be longer than ten minutes, will you?'

He went out, leaving her alone to marvel at his decision. Her pulses were still racing unsteadily. She had been so sure he was going to kiss her.

Dressing quickly in silk lingerie, she slid into the black jodhpurs and was pleased with the fit. They emphasised her long slim legs, and the narrow curve of waist to hip. The black sweater was warm, and the long black leather riding boots rather erotic.

Jean-Marc's grey eyes told her he thought the outfit very erotic when she entered the drawing-room, but he said nothing, and now that she was getting to know him she knew he didn't have to.

They went out through the kitchens. A hive of activity, they were a vast cavernous echo of days gone by, with a fireplace big enough to roast a whole deer on a spit, copper pans gleaming along the ancient stone walls, and a long oak table dominating the centre of the enormous stone floor.

'Bonjour, Monsieur Jean-Marc!'

'Ça va, Monsieur Jean-Marc?'

Various members of staff called greetings to him, their faces filled with warmth and their eyes with respect as he strode through with Alicia beside him.

Jean-Marc smiled back and stopped to inspect the croissants and brioche being freshly baked in the vast stone ovens by a plump woman with salt and pepper hair.

He introduced Alicia to them, then led her out through the large back door to a vast cobbled courtyard littered with straw, the early morning air fresh and sunlit, a faint mist on the rolling French fields around them.

'Quite the lord of the manor!' Alicia commented drily, but she was impressed, and slid a shy little glance at him.

'Look at me like that again,' he drawled softly, 'and I might exercise my droit de seigneur!'

She flushed, lowering her lashes. 'Did you inherit all of this?'

'I inherited the estate two years ago when my parents died,' he told her as they walked towards the stables. 'It was quite a shock for me. They were killed in a car crash.'

'I'm sorry,' she said, studying his tough profile.

'Life goes on,' he said deeply in French, and then, 'But I was brought up here, and I love the place. The only problem is that I have no children to inherit it, and I am the last in the Brissac line.'

Alicia looked at him sharply, aware of the deep contents of that statement, but he didn't seem to be aware of it, his face coolly unreadable as he strolled with his customary arrogance beside her.

'And you, Alicia.' He stopped at the stable gate, one strong hand resting on the latch as he looked at it. 'You say your sister is your only relative. Your parents died . . . ?'

'When I was seventeen.'

His dark lashes flickered. 'A tender age.' He pushed the gate open, let her walk through first, then followed her, saying casually, 'Were you lucky enough to have someone to turn to?'

Alicia stiffened, her face growing cold. 'My sister. Who else?'

'So you met this man later?' he asked, running a hand through his black hair.

'What man?' she said at once, stopping, suddenly breathless.

Jean-Marc stopped too, and looked down into her face. 'The man who broke your heart.'

White, appalled, she looked away from him and found herself unable to do anything other than stare at the cobbled stones, the straw.

'Did he break your heart?' he asked deeply, frowning. 'Or did he just hurt you badly enough to make you unable to trust anyone else?'

She stared at the cobbled stones, quite still.

'There has to be a man somewhere, Alicia.' He touched her dark hair, pushing an unruly strand away from her face. 'You're so beautiful. You have so much drive, so much energy. And so much passion. Why would any woman as tempestuous as you channel all that passion into her work?'

She blinked, stared at the stones, said stiffly, 'I take it you like solving puzzles.'

'It wasn't hard to figure out. The day I met you, you gave me a look filled with such rage and hatred that I practically stopped breathing.'

'Lindy had just told me what you'd done to her!' she said fiercely, raising her head. 'Of course I was angry!'

'Not that angry.' He studied her face with thoughtful eyes. 'You were breathing fire, Alicia. I could feel it like a physical force. I've never sensed such rage before in my adult life.'

Hot colour swept her face. 'It was justifiable, considering what you'd done to Lindy.'

'I did nothing to Lindy,' he said gently, watching her face. 'Nothing except pay her a little too much attention when she was lonely and at a loose end.'

She gave an angry laugh. 'If you expect me to believe that after——'

'She was alone here with me,' he cut in, 'and miles away from home. I was alone too. What was I supposed to do—ignore her? I took her out for dinner once or twice and——'

'And kissed her!'

His mouth twisted and he said flatly, 'Alicia, I'm going to have to disillusion you. I'm sorry. Lindy kissed me. Once. On the mouth when I was barely aware of her as more than a child. I was so shocked, I just stared at her. Then I thought—I must handle this properly. I must not give her a sense of guilt. So I tried to defuse the situation by kissing her on the cheek as though her kiss had not been fired by—more passionate motives.' His dark brows rose. 'She misinterpreted it, slid on to my lap, and I was stupid enough to throw her off and tell her very sharply to go to bed.'

Alicia believed him, however much she didn't want to, because the ring of sincerity was matched by the regret in his grey eyes as he told her the truth.

'I over-reacted,' he said with a broad shrug. 'Then I felt guilty and tried to make it up to her the following day, by taking her to dinner. She misinterpreted that, too, but she didn't show it. By the time she *did* show how dangerously she had misinterpreted it—it was too late.'

'So you were never actually—involved with her?' Alicia watched his face intently.

'Never,' he said deeply, and there was a brief silence between them. The birds were singing, and the faint mist on the fields around the estate had risen, allowing warm sunlight to flood in.

Alicia accepted what he said about Lindy. What else could she do? He had obviously been sincere. It hurt to think of Lindy's pain—but it was now sadly obvious that it had just been a schoolgirl crush on an older man.

'Now it's your turn,' Jean-Marc said softly, watching her.

She looked up, frowning. 'My turn?'

'To confess,' he said with a wry smile, and touched her cheek. 'You realised it was something of an exchange, didn't you?'

Alicia stiffened, tried to move away. 'I don't know what you're talking about!'

'Alicia,' he said, catching her arm, his face grim, 'you must tell me about him.'

Angry, she looked away, staring at a horse as it poked its head out of a stable door. 'It's none of your business, Jean-Marc!'

'Isn't it?' His dark brows rose. 'As far as I can see, he's partly responsible for making you the woman you are. Or rather—he's responsible for the gloss of cold hauteur, the aristocratic reserve. You use that as a defence, don't you, Alicia? To keep men away, shut out all advances.'

'Why should I bother to do that?' she said scathingly.

'Because you're so stunning,' he said coolly. 'And if you were obviously passionate too, you'd have to spend all your time fighting men off.'

She caught her breath. 'You should be a psychologist!'

'It follows,' he said, eyes narrowing, 'that you must have been very openly passionate at seventeen. And if that is what you turned against in yourself—that's the very thing that must have hurt you. Your passionate nature.'

She stared, her face draining of all colour.

'That's it, isn't it?' he said suddenly, frowning. 'You were seduced——'

Her eyes blazed with sudden long-buried rage. 'Yes, that's it, Jean-Marc! I was seduced! I was

seventeen and passionate—and he was just like you!
Arrogant, conceited and with more sex appeal than
he knew what to do with!' She breathed erratically,
her pulses thudding. 'He spent three months
treating me like a princess until I gave in, and when
I did—he left me!' She was shaking suddenly,
almost unable to stand as the rage flooded her veins.
'He walked out on me the day after I gave in, and
I vowed then that no man would ever do that to
me again!' With a hoarse cry, she turned and ran
from him, hot tears stinging her eyes as she fled,
breathing hoarsely.

He caught her, of course, his arms around her
waist as he pulled her close to his powerful chest,
keeping her there even though she fought with
hoarse cries of uncontrollable emotion.

'*Chérie . . . !*' He fought to keep her close, saying
urgently, 'You must forgive yourself. You were
young, innocent——'

'And now I'm not innocent any more!' she
choked out, struggling against his strong arms.

'Yes, you are,' he said bitingly. 'Yes, you are,
because he never made love to you! He only seduced
you and walked away, and that makes you innocent,
chérie! That makes you an innocent victim of a
ruthless man's selfishness and spite!'

Wincing, she whispered fiercely, 'I won't be a
victim! I refuse to be a victim!'

'We all make mistakes, *chérie*,' he said deeply.
'We're all human enough to do that.'

Tears burned in her eyes and throat. 'Not me! I
won't make mistakes like that! Never again,
never——'

'You can't make yourself perfect, Alicia,' he said, taking her face in his strong hands. 'You deny yourself everything that is wonderful in life if you do. You deny yourself love, affection, spontaneity, children—you deny life, *chérie*, because nothing in life is perfect.'

Her mouth quivered. She felt helpless. 'But...what am I supposed to do?'

'Forgive yourself,' he said gently, 'for being imperfect.'

Alicia swallowed, and lowered her wet lashes, staring at his hard chest and, as her hands rested on it, she felt the strong steady heartbeat beneath the black sweater he wore.

'Can we...' she struggled to recover her self-control '... can we ride now? I—I'd like to end this conversation, if you don't mind.'

He was silent for a moment, studying her bent head. Then he said, 'So long as you think about what I've said, Alicia. Will you think about it?'

Alicia nodded, wiped a tear from her high cheek. Jean-Marc watched her with a slow smile touching his hard mouth, and his grey eyes flickered over her.

'You have great dignity, Alicia,' he said softly.

She shot him a startled look, her face colouring. For some reason the way he had spoken left her feeling breathless, and as she stared into his eyes she saw them darken.

His strong hands tightened on her waist. 'When you look at me like that,' he said roughly, 'I want to be very imperfect with you, Alicia.'

Her heart skipped a beat. 'Don't...'

'I gave my word that I would not kiss you,' he said under his breath. 'But you did not give your word that you would not kiss me.'

She gave a soft laugh against her will. 'I hardly needed to...'

'Then will you kiss me?' he asked, his charm devastating. 'Just once. One kiss.'

Alicia felt a tremor go through her, and, looking at his hard mouth through her lashes, she slowly stood on tiptoe and pressed her mouth against it.

He made a rough sound and parted her lips with his, and she submitted with a sudden wave of desire that caught her off guard, her mouth opening and her arms going blindly around his neck.

With a sudden gasp, she stepped back, face flushed and dark eyes glittering with passion, her mouth softly bruised and her legs trembling beneath her.

'That's enough!' she said huskily.

He gave a slow smile. He was darkly flushed. *'Comme tu veux,'* he drawled, and took her hand, pressing it to his hard, passionate mouth. 'But there may come a day, Alicia, when I lose my head and break my promise. Will you forgive me, then? For making you see how completely you are mine, and how very much I want all that passion you've kept locked away for so long.'

Alicia's heart skipped beats, her mouth quivering as he stared.

'Will you forgive yourself,' he asked softly, 'for wanting me in return?'

Her face flamed and she did not answer him, staring at the strong column of his throat, her heart thudding and her pulses racing, and knew she could not answer that question herself.

His jet flew her back to London that afternoon. Of course, she had to return the following Friday. He had extracted that promise from her without any argument. She had accepted the job, and it was too late to back out now.

If I back out, he'll only find some other reason to see me, she realised with a faint ironic smile.

When she returned, she busied herself with her usual work, and also with plans for the wedding. Dominique had given her her clippings, and Alicia sat at home every night, leafing through them for design ideas.

The dress slowly began to come together in her head. After dozens of preliminary sketches, she finally hit on the right style, and began to work on that exclusively, drawing ideas from the top fashions of the last year to make sure it had the stamp of the era.

Once she had the nucleus of the bridal gown, Alicia was able to begin preparatory sketches for the bridesmaids' dresses. The ballroom would be more difficult. But as it was still two months till the wedding, Alicia felt she had plenty of time to work on that later.

Alicia had lunch with her sister Susannah on Thursday. They ate at a pretty restaurant on the river at Richmond.

'I'll tell Lindy you're working for Brissac,' Susannah assured her. 'She'll come to terms with it. Don't worry.'

'I wish I could tell her myself,' Alicia sighed. 'But I can't help feeling it would only make it worse.'

'Quite right,' Susannah agreed. 'And speaking of passing on news personally—have you heard from David?'

Alicia shook her dark head.

'He's gone back to Eileen,' Susannah told her. 'Remember the girl he dropped when he met you? Blonde girl, works in the High Street. Lives just round the corner from here.'

'I remember her,' Alicia said, nodding slowly. 'And I think he's probably right to go back to her. She's much more suitable for David than I ever was.'

'You didn't fit in with his life,' Susannah remarked, studying her oddly. 'You tend not to fit in, don't you, Alicia? You were always different from the rest of the family. Even your looks are a throwback.'

She gave a wry smile. 'I was a cuckoo.'

'Mummy always said the gypsies left you...' Susannah laughed.

Alicia flew to Paris the following night, thinking about that conversation with her sister. David's decision to go back to Eileen was obviously the right one. She hoped he would be happy. No doubt he would marry the girl and settle down in Richmond—something Alicia could never have been happy doing. She needed excitement, action, power and the bright busy world of fashion. If she had married a man like David and tried to settle in Richmond, she would have turned into Hedda Gabler and destroyed everything she touched with her frustration and resentment.

The prospect was an unpleasant one, and she shuddered, looking out of the limousine window as the car sped out of Paris and on to the motorway leading to the Loire.

She thought about Susannah's remarks about not fitting in. It was true. Her mother had been a short, plump, homely woman. Her father had been average height, thick-built and blond. And Susannah had inherited their looks, with her dark brown hair and lazy, cheerful outlook on life.

But Alicia? Alicia was tall, slender, fine-boned and her energy levels were at odds with the rest of her rather laid-back family. In fact, everything about her was different, she realised with a frown. Not just her looks and energy, but her whole personality, including her love of beauty and fine art, of fashion and theatre and travel—and, most of all, her ambition.

Is that why I got engaged to David? she wondered with a shock. Precisely *because* he was completely at odds with my true self? As though, by marrying a man who regarded me as a creature from another planet, I would feel at home, as I did with the family who never understood me.

The gates of Château Brissac swung open with a powerful electronic buzz. The limousine purred through, and Alicia's heart began to beat faster as she saw the aristocratic turrets of the château pierce the moonlit sky.

'Bonsoir, mademoiselle.' The butler showed her in again, his distinguished face lined with age. 'Monsieur Brissac has arranged a light supper for ten o'clock. Please meet him in the dining-room then.'

How easily I swing back into French, she thought, going upstairs followed by the impeccably dressed chauffeur, who was becoming as familiar to her as the butler.

Alicia had brought two suitcases this time. One contained clothes, cosmetics and so on, the other all her sketches, swatches of material, photographs of pearl detail designs, and various other essential ingredients, including some back copies of *Vogue* and *Tatler* detailing other very fashionable weddings.

At ten, she found the dining-room, and went in. The room was silent, panelled with dark wood, and very elegant. A silver candelabrum lit the long mahogany table. Silver cutlery gleamed in the flickering light.

Alicia frowned, then saw Jean-Marc, asleep.

Her face softened. Silently, she closed the door and tiptoed over the deep red carpet. Sinking down on the long dark brown sofa, she stared at him.

His breathing was even and deep. He had taken his evening jacket off, slung it over the back of a chair, and loosened his black tie. The top two buttons of his shirt were open. His black hair was tousled, his chiselled features made vulnerable by sleep.

Alicia ran her fingers over his shoulder, lightly, so as not to wake him, then over his chest. She encountered a heartbeat. Human, then, she thought with a faint smile.

His steel-grey eyes opened.

Her heart stopped beating.

For a second, they just looked into each other's eyes.

'Was I asleep?' Jean-Marc asked deeply.

'Yes.' Her voice was husky. 'I woke you. I'm sorry.'

'I've had an exhausting week.' His hard mouth was so attractive. 'I only just had time to shower and dress before you arrived.'

Her black lashes flickered. 'Problems at work?'

A sardonic smile lit his grey eyes. *'Comme toujours!'*

'Your offices are in Paris, aren't they?' She frowned a little.

He inclined his dark head, lying still, his powerful body relaxed.

'Surely you need the limousine, then?' Alicia said. 'How did you get back tonight?'

'Helicopter,' he said coolly. 'It's quicker. I generally take it. And I have an apartment on the Faubourg, just in case I need to stay overnight.'

'An apartment? Then why were you staying at the Ritz...?' Alicia stared into his tough face and suddenly caught her breath at the grim look in his grey eyes. 'My God! You planned it!' She tried to stand up.

'Wait!' He caught her wrist like a shot, pulled her back down beside him, laughing sardonically. 'I didn't plan it. It just happened.'

Anger shot through her. 'You deliberately booked into the Ritz with the specific intention of destroying my engagement!'

'Not true,' he said flatly, holding her when she struggled. 'Alicia, don't lose that famous temper of yours!' He laughed, one powerful arm going around her and holding her close to his chest as he drawled against her hair, 'Look—I was at the Ritz for a business lunch. It wound up at three, and as

I came out of the restaurant I saw you checking in.'

'You devious, manipulative——' Alicia was so angry that she could barely speak, her voice muffled against his chest.

'I decided to book a room myself and see what happened.' His hard voice overrode hers. 'You'd already caught my attention at that party, Alicia.'

She pushed at his shoulders, sitting up in his powerful arms. 'You lied to me!'

'Did I?' His dark brows rose mockingly. 'I don't recall ever telling you I did not have an apartment in Paris.'

Furious, she said, 'That's not the point! You made it seem as though it was just coincidence you happened to be staying at the Ritz when——'

'It was coincidence,' he said flatly. 'In fact, it felt like fate.'

She fell silent, staring at his tough, arrogant face. He was so attractive to her that she hated herself for the way she found herself looking at him, at his hard mouth and broad shoulders and the tanned column of his throat.

'I believe in fate,' Jean-Marc said softly, watching her through heavy-lidded eyes. 'Do you?'

'Sometimes,' she said, her pulses picking up a different beat.

'Yes.' His strong hand lifted to her face, touched her high cheek. 'I'd thought about you all week, you see. I remembered you vividly from that party. When I saw you in Paris I felt fate hit us both.'

Alicia stared, her breathing quickening.

'You have to trust your instincts,' Jean-Marc said softly, and suddenly his strong hands were on her slim shoulders, pulling her down slowly, very slowly towards him.

Her eyes darkened with sudden fierce passion.

Jean-Marc caught the flare of fire in her eyes. With a rough sound of excitement, he pulled her into his arms, her body against his on the couch, and they kissed with slow sensuality, exploring each other's mouths as his strong hands curved on her slim hips and hers threaded helplessly through his thick black hair. It felt so good to be in his arms, to feel his heart thudding against her full breasts, to taste that hard mouth again and feel the warm, drugging sensuality of his kiss reach a new intimacy that was so deeply pleasurable that she found her heart racing as his mouth moved over hers again and again. Their eyes were closed and the intoxicating sweetness was flooding their veins as they clung together and she felt his hands move up to frame her face, making her feel deeply wanted.

When he drew his dark head back, he was breathing fast and he was darkly flushed as he looked down at her, eyes narrowing on her aroused face.

'You're not fighting,' he said under his breath. 'But that's not my fault. And I don't want you to walk out now that our agreement has been broken.'

Alicia flushed, angry with herself. 'I was caught off guard!' She slid out of his embrace, sitting up, her dark head bent, deeply aware that she had wanted that kiss very badly and been helpless to resist when he pulled her into his arms. 'And our agreement isn't broken. Just slightly damaged. And...it won't happen again.'

He studied her in silence for a moment, then said deeply, 'Alicia—would you do something for me?'

'That depends on what it is,' she said huskily, avoiding his eyes, deeply aware of her complicity in that brief, passionate kiss and of his immediate recognition of that. It must have been the sudden dark emotion in her eyes...

'Wear your hair loose,' he said softly, 'while you are here.'

Turning, she stared at him. 'Loose...!'

He gave a slow, sardonic smile. 'I like it loose. Would you mind? Just while you are here. Whenever you're at this château. Wear it loose.' His grey eyes met hers intently as he added, 'For me.'

Her heart skipped several beats at the look in his eyes, and the deeply romantic request. For a second, she couldn't speak, then she found her hands moving slowly to her black hair, taking the pins out in silence until the long straight silk of her hair tumbled in feminine glory around her slender shoulders.

'Thank you,' Jean-Marc said softly, and then sat up, slid a hand over hers, and got to his feet.

Shocked, Alicia stared up at him, deeply vulnerable. She had expected him to kiss her again, start to make love to her, say something, do something...

'I'll ring for dinner.' Jean-Marc was standing, hands thrust in black trouser pockets, watching her with an odd expression in his eyes. 'And tomorrow I will show you the office I have had converted for your use. Is that OK?'

Slowly, she nodded, and wondered why he was letting her off so lightly. Had he wanted to, he could have made love to her just then. She had wanted that kiss from the moment she saw him, lying here asleep on the sofa, and Jean-Marc had sensed that deep undercurrent of helpless desire from the moment he woke up and saw her...

CHAPTER SEVEN

NEXT morning, Alicia was woken bright and early
by a tap on her bedroom door. Rolling over in the
vast four-poster bed, her black hair sliding sensu-
ously over her bare shoulders, she called sleepily,
'Come in . . . I mean, *entrez*!'

The door opened, and her heart skipped beats as
Jean-Marc appeared, looking gorgeous in black
riding clothes, a smile on his hard mouth as he
strolled arrogantly towards the bed and put
Dominique's riding outfit down for her.

'Fifteen minutes?' he asked softly.

Alicia nodded, breathless.

He turned and strode coolly out, closing the door
behind him.

They rode the same horses they had last time.
Alicia's mount was an elegant black mare with high-
bred anklebones and a glossy black mane. Of
course, Jean-Marc rode a full blooded Arab
stallion, and as they thundered across the rolling
parkland of the Brissac estate Alicia secretly cast
admiring, excited, proud looks at him through her
lashes.

They got back in time for breakfast. Both
sweating and exhilarated, they were laughing as they
strode through the kitchens, their faces alive with
the powerful blood beat of hard exercise and the
fresh morning air.

'I'm ravenous!' Jean-Marc told her as he opened the dining-room door for her. 'And ready for a busy day!'

Alicia laughed, excited by his presence and his personality as she walked past him, sexy in her long black boots. 'Is Dominique still staying here?'

'Mais bien sûr!' Dominique called, grinning at her from the dining-room table. 'I'm staying here until the wedding.'

'You're lazy and spoilt and I adore you!' Jean-Marc drawled, bending to drop a kiss on her dark head and ruffle her long curls, and Alicia watched, noticing again how fond he was of the girl.

After breakfast, she went up to her room to shower and change. Dressing in a white wool dress, she looked intensely feminine, especially with her dark hair left loose. Left loose for Jean-Marc...the phrase made her heart beat faster. She suddenly felt so beautiful.

Her office was at the end of the west wing. It was a beautiful high-ceilinged room with mahogany desk, a smart filing cabinet, telephones, a fax machine, and a vast stack of drawing materials flown in by helicopter, he told her, from a top designer in Paris.

'You should have everything you need,' Jean-Marc told her flatly, impeccably dressed in a grey business suit, dark red silk tie, and gold watch chain across his taut stomach. 'A friend of mine in the fashion industry organised it all for you, at my request.'

'I'm impressed,' Alicia said with a wry smile. 'This is exactly what I have in my London headquarters.'

He smiled, grey eyes flickering over her. 'Head-quarters...' he murmured, as though it pleased him.

'But I'll need somewhere to make up the garments.' Alicia frowned, glancing around.

'I've arranged for you to have unlimited use of the facilities at Ballatria in Paris,' he said coolly.

Her eyes widened. Ballatria was in the upper echelons of French fashion, and their reputation was as exclusive as their prices. Those hallowed portals admitted the most famous and beautiful women in the world, and Alicia knew their cutters, fitters, all facilities would be superb.

'If that's too far for minor alterations,' Jean-Marc strode to a connecting door, 'there are facilities here.'

Alicia walked through and caught her breath, staring at the streamlined equipment he had obviously gone to a great deal of trouble and expense to have brought here and fitted.

'Jean-Marc...!' She stared up into his tough face. 'I know you're very wealthy, but surely——'

'It cost me nothing, *chérie*,' he cut in with a sardonic smile. 'It was an exchange. A business deal, shall we say? I have a lot of friends, and they help me out sometimes, just as I help them.'

Looking around the rooms with a dazed expression, she itched to get to work. The view from this window was superb, the offices comfortable, and the work ahead growing more exciting with each moment.

'You remembered,' Jean-Marc said softly, touching her hair.

Startled, she looked at him, touching her hair self-consciously. 'Oh, yes... my hair.'

'You look quite lovely,' he said, and then his eyes darkened, lowering suddenly to her mouth.

Her heart raced. An involuntary quiver shot through her. She felt the rush of sweet desire, and Jean-Marc saw it flash like fire in her dark eyes.

He made a rough sound under his breath and pulled her into his arms. Her mouth opened beneath his, and suddenly his hands were hard on her hips, holding her soft, pliant body against his and they kissed deeply, both drowning in a moment of heart-racing freedom as the blood soared through their veins and their bodies seemed to melt into each other.

Without warning, he drew back, his grey eyes opaque with desire. 'If you wanted to stop me, you would—wouldn't you, Alicia?'

She felt helpless, staring into his grey eyes, her body weak with burning desire.

'But you don't stop me,' he said softly. 'So either you're beginning to accept what is between us—or you're getting ready to surrender.'

'Neither!' she flashed with sudden defiance. 'I just find your brand of sex appeal difficult to resist. It means nothing, though, does it, Jean-Marc? It's just another drug on the market!'

His mouth hardened. 'If I put you under attack right now, you wouldn't be able to defend yourself and you know it.'

'That has more to do with you than with me!' she said hotly.

He watched her grimly. 'Don't lie to yourself, Alicia. It's not worthy of you. You want me as much as I want you, and sooner or later you're going to admit it.'

Hot colour flooded her face and she pulled away from him, her mouth tight with bitter self-loathing. He was implying that her passion matched his. She hated him for forcing her to face it.

'Don't drive yourself crazy over it!' he drawled with soft mockery. 'That's my job.'

Bitterly, she looked at him. 'Is this the way you always operate, Jean-Marc? Using underhand methods, trickery, torment and even physical force?'

He looked at her oddly. 'No, Alicia. Only since I met you.'

Her heart skipped a beat as she stared at him in shocked silence.

'You have work to do and so have I,' Jean-Marc drawled, and ran a long finger to her mouth before turning, striding to the door. 'I'll send Dominique to you!'

Alicia watched him walk out of the room. As the door closed, her fingers went to her mouth, fingering the taste of his passion, and she realised that her own passion was growing with each moment she spent in his company.

Forcing herself to settle down, the discipline of years flooded to her rescue to stop her dwelling on Jean-Marc Brissac's mind, a subject she was beginning to realise was as complex as it was fascinating. Dominique arrived a few minutes later, and they spent three very busy and enjoyable hours working before the printer arrived and took their format away, promising the invitations by Monday morning. Dominique gasped over Alicia's designs for the bridal gown and bridesmaids' dresses. She also made one or two suggestions that Alicia thought showed great flair.

'I've often thought of going into the fashion industry,' Dominique confessed when Alicia praised her ideas. 'Jean-Marc's very encouraging, too. He said he'd get me a job in one of the major houses.'

'But you want to get married first?' Alicia asked, smiling.

Dominique laughed. 'Of course! You're not a woman unless you've got a man you really love!'

Alicia studied her, confusion in her dark eyes. Was she right? Or was it just because she was eighteen, in love and planning her wedding?

'There's a saying,' Dominique warmed to her subject, 'which goes: "to love is nothing, to be loved is something, to love and be loved is everything".'

Alicia's dark lashes flickered, then she said lightly, 'There's another saying: "to thine own self be true".' Her dark eyes rested gently on the girl's beautiful face. 'We all have different needs, Dominique. And we must fulfil them as best we can.'

But the girl's words stayed in her mind, and she frowned as she worked on through the day, breaking for coffee every hour on the hour. Was she fulfilled? Her own needs had been syphoned into work for so long that she had forgotten the deep well of passion she possessed until Jean-Marc came along. If that was a real need, a valid part of her—surely it must find expression and fulfilment?

They worked through without a real break till six o'clock that night. Alicia's shoulders ached, but she felt the exhilaration of achievement and knew they had laid some solid foundations.

'Jean-Marc always serves drinks in the drawing-room at six.' Dominique told her as they walked back through the corridors to the central part of the château. 'And I could certainly do with a glass of wine!'

Alicia smiled. 'Yes, why not? We've earned one!'

'We'll have to think about the drinks, too,' Dominique mused. 'I think Laurent-Perrier vintage champagne is very fashionable this year...'

Alicia laughed, opened the drawing-room door, and saw Isabelle Janvier kissing Jean-Marc Brissac passionately on the mouth.

With an indrawn horrified breath, she shut the door again.

White, she stood frozen, her dark eyes reflecting shock.

'Alicia?' Dominique's voice was worried. 'What's wrong?'

For a second, she didn't understand the French language, and just stared at the girl, her face blank, skin taut over delicate bones, while the knife of jealousy thrust searingly in her heart.

The door opened.

Alicia stepped back, staring in horror at Jean-Marc as he stared down at her. Red lipstick stained his hard cheek. His eyes were fierce silver and his face darkly flushed.

'You should have knocked,' he said slowly, and she felt her face tightening in appalling jealous rage.

'Why?' Dominique was frowning. 'What's going on?'

'Nothing.' Alicia struggled to pull the cloak of icy dignity back around her shoulders, her face closing into an aristocratic mask. 'I just interrupted your godfather in a private conversation. Forgive me. You're quite right. I should have knocked.' She turned to leave.

He caught her arm. 'You were going to have a drink before changing for dinner?' His eyes were narrowed and saw far too much. 'In that case—come in.'

She gave an icy smile, aware that her hands were shaking uncontrollably, and immediately put them behind her back, assuming a cool businesslike stance.

'Really, it's not necessary,' she drawled, affecting indifference.

'I insist,' he said in a voice like steel.

She could hardly argue. Alicia walked coolly into the drawing-room, and even she was unprepared for the white-hot burn of jealousy as she saw Isabelle Janvier's perfect face.

'Mademoiselle Holt...' Isabelle had repaired her red lipstick, her face flawless once again, no emotion whatever in the crystalline eyes.

'Good evening,' Alicia said tightly.

Dominique came in slowly behind her, eyes flashing round the room, sensing the atmosphere but apparently not understanding it as she gave Alicia a curious frown.

'Isabelle is on location here,' Jean-Marc said coolly, pouring two glasses of red wine. 'Filming at Château Clemet, ten kilometres from us.'

'How interesting,' Alicia drawled. 'What's the film?'

'*La Belle Dame Sans Merci*,' Isabelle said, relaxing, sitting back in her armchair and pushing a swath of ice-blonde hair back. 'It's a medieval film. I have very beautiful costumes.'

'French?' Alicia asked, her smile tense.

'American,' Jean-Marc drawled with a sardonic smile, striding coolly to Alicia and handing her a glass of red wine. 'Isabelle is one of our greatest cross-over actresses.'

'Yes, I've seen many of your films.' Alicia could not look at Jean-Marc in case he saw the jealousy in her eyes. 'You're quite exceptional.'

Isabelle's perfect mouth curved. 'Thank you,' she said softly.

They talked politely for fifteen minutes. Alicia's nerves were in shreds. She had never experienced jealousy in her life before. Not like this. Not so consuming, like a fire raging in her stomach, sending poison into her veins and making her want to scream at Jean-Marc, How dare you do this to me? How dare you...?

'Well,' Alicia put her wine glass down when she deemed it politely acceptable to leave, 'I'm afraid I'm exhausted and in need of a long hot bath. Would you excuse me?'

'Yes, of course.' Isabelle smiled, tilting her ice-blonde head. 'I hope to see you again while you're here.'

Alicia's smile froze in her eyes. 'I hope so too.' Turning, she left the room without even glancing at Jean-Marc, until he held the door open for her.

He gave her an astute, narrow-eyed look as she passed him. Alicia treated him to her tightest smile and felt great satisfaction in seeing his brows shoot up.

Ten minutes later, she was seething in the great bath, her face scarlet amid the steam, scrubbing her fingernails with a brush and cursing Jean-Marc Brissac. Damn him! How many more women did he have carrying fierce desire for him? And how many did he have under attack at any one time?

She had been a fool ever to come here. Now that she had seen him with Isabelle she realised that she *had* accepted for personal reasons. It had never just been the job that tempted her. It had been Jean-Marc himself, his hard mouth and long, skilful hands and that powerful body that knew how to make her feel every inch a woman.

He's right, she thought, horrified. I do want him.

When she emerged from the bathroom in a white wrap, he was sitting on the bed.

Alicia felt the rush of fierce, shaking hatred return. 'Must you keep doing this?' she demanded.

'Doing what, Alicia?' he asked softly, eyes taking in the rigid, angry stance of her body. 'I knocked and received no answer, so I came in.'

'What do you want?' she asked tightly, folding her arms, acutely aware of her nudity, the steamy scented texture of her flesh beneath the wrap.

'I came to see why I got the icy treatment just now.' He was watching her closely. 'And why you were so impeccably polite to Isabelle when you obviously dislike her.'

'I don't dislike her,' she said, her tone rigid with choked emotion.

'Come on, Alicia. I know you too well for this to work.' He got to his feet, strolling coolly towards her, his mouth as hard as his grey eyes. 'You've been melting, slowly, and softening. Suddenly the haughty aristocrat is back, and your voice is dripping with ice. Why?'

Hot angry colour swept through her face. 'I don't know what you're talking about!'

He towered over her, caught her chin, forced her to face him. 'I know what it is, Alicia,' he said softly. 'I'll say it if you want me to. But I'd rather hear it from you.'

'I've had a hard day!' she said thickly, trying to tear her face from his hard-fingered grasp. 'I just want to rest and relax! I was forced to be polite to Isabelle when I was tired! Is it so surprising that I——'

'You were jealous,' he said softly.

'I was not jealous!' she denied hotly, trembling with sudden rage. 'I was just tired and the last thing I wanted to do was——'

'You were jealous, Alicia.'

She slapped his face without thinking, her mouth trembling with rage.

His head jerked back and his eyes darkened. 'Yes!' he said thickly. 'You were jealous!'

Her eyes flared with dark fire. 'Go to hell, you conceited, arrogant bastard!' she swore hoarsely, and started hitting him in blind fury, her hands raining blows on his powerful shoulders and broad chest.

'God...!' he bit out roughly, and caught her flailing wrists, pinned them behind her back and jerked her hard against his body, ignoring her violent cries of rage as his hard mouth covered hers.

Alicia struggled, tearing her mouth from his, hating him so much that she was shaking from head to foot, and when he picked her up in his powerful arms and carried her over to the bed she started to make harsh noises in the back of her throat that sounded like a wild animal in the throes of passion.

'You bastard!' she choked out hoarsely as he laid her on the bed. 'I hate you...hate you...!'

He joined her, his eyes fierce, but her hands were already linking behind his strong head, pulling him down until his mouth met hers and she unleashed her hunger on him, her fingers tangling in his black hair as she kissed him with all the pent-up desire she had never dared release.

He made a ragged sound of excitement under his breath, his mouth possessing hers with absolute mastery, and, as he dominated her, so she moaned, her heart thudding out of control and she surrendered entirely to the waves of hot sensation flooding her veins.

Blindly, she was tugging at his silk tie, her hands shaking on the buttons of his shirt, tearing it open, gasping in hot, shaking excitement as she found his chest, her fingers sliding over the tanned flesh and the thick black hair.

'I hate you!' she moaned, practically tearing the last buttons in her need to release the tumult of emotion she felt. 'You swine...!'

'Yes...!' he whispered thickly against her mouth. 'Oh, yes...take it out on me...let me have it all!'

Alicia felt his strong hands move up to cover her breasts and gave a hoarse cry of need, falling back, her head flung back on the pillow, breath coming in quick gasps as Jean-Marc closed in on her, his mouth a firm sensual line of determination as he pulled the white wrap open to bare her to the waist.

With a harsh sound of need, he bent his dark head to her bare breast and she groaned, aching to feel his hot mouth take her nipple, arching slightly until she felt it slide into his mouth and the hot needles of excitement rushed through her as she went dizzy, body pulsing with hot blood, her mind completely lost in the sweet sensations he invoked.

Suddenly, he raised his dark head, staring at her in silence. She stared back, eyes half-closed and fevered, her face deeply flushed.

'You were jealous,' he asked shakingly, 'weren't you? Admit it! For God's sake...'

'Yes!' she said bitterly, eyes smouldering. 'Does that satisfy you, Jean-Marc? Does it make you feel like a man?'

He looked at her grimly. 'I don't ask you for that reason. I need to know because I have so little else to go on. You have no need to be jealous of Isabelle. But I do have need to be jealous of your passionate nature, and wonder where it will lead if not to me.'

Alicia frowned, not understanding, her pulses drumming as she tried to take the words in.

'I've woken a sleeping tiger,' he said grimly. 'I don't want to find some other man being the recipient of your rediscovered passion, Alicia. Is that so unreasonable?'

Bitterly, she said, 'Do you want more than one mistress, Jean-Marc? You have Isabelle. You certainly don't need me!'

'Isabelle was once my mistress,' he admitted. 'But that was a long time ago. We're just friends now, Alicia, for all that you saw us kiss.'

She gave a hoarse laugh. 'You really expect me to believe that?'

'You know it already,' he said deeply, and pressed a strong hand below her left breast, above her heart. 'Here.'

Staring into his grey eyes, she felt suddenly unsure, breathless.

'You were jealous,' he said thickly, 'because you know we belong together. You hated me for kissing Isabelle. Tell me what you thought when you left us.'

Dazed, she heard her voice whisper, 'I thought "How dare he . . . ?"'

'How dare he kiss another woman?' A sardonic smile touched his hard mouth. 'You see? You know, Alicia, what really lies between us. But that makes you my property, too. Don't ever let me find you with another man, *chérie*, or you will see my jealousy, and it will be even more ferocious than yours.' His hard mouth closed over hers, taking possession with such blazing authority that she felt herself surrender immediately, her mouth sliding open with a soft moan as he kissed her deeply, his hard body pinning hers to the bed.

His hands slowly stroked down her body, curving over hip and thigh, and she quivered at his touch, filled with warm, sensual, drugging sensation, her head dizzy again as the pulse grew louder and she could hear her heart beating audibly.

When Jean-Marc lifted his head this time, there was the glitter of triumph in his grey eyes as he said thickly, 'You're mine! I could take you now and you wouldn't fight. Tell me that . . . tell me you surrender without conditions!'

She opened her heavy eyelids, breathing erratically.

'Tell me, Alicia,' he commanded, mouth hard.

'Yes,' she whispered bitterly, hating him, 'I surrender!'

A smile touched his hard mouth. He kissed her once, then released her, resting on one elbow as he looked into her surprised face. 'I have to go away tonight, Alicia,' he said. 'I won't be back for at least three weeks.'

The colour drained from her face. 'You're kidding . . . !'

He smiled, slid a hand possessively over her waist. 'You'll miss me, then?'

'Where are you going?' she asked, ignoring his question.

'Japan, Australia and America,' he said with a wry grimace. 'There's a whirlwind blowing up in my corporation, Alicia, and it's time I swooped in on those three headquarters. I'm starting with Tokyo, because they need the biggest rocket put under them.'

'A week in each country?' she asked. 'You'll get terrible jet lag.'

He laughed softly. 'I wish you could be there to soothe me to sleep every night.' His grey gaze flickered over her face, then he said on impulse, 'Come with me.'

She caught her breath, tempted beyond endurance, just the thought of spending so much time with him in such fabulous cities more than she could bear.

But she refused. 'You know very well that I won't.'

'Because of work?' He was teasing her, his smile lazily mocking.

'No, because of you!' she said, a half-smile on her mouth.

He laughed, and then his face grew serious as he said deeply, 'Alicia, although I enjoy this war, I did believe we had come to an understanding that might lead to an armed truce.'

'While you continue to try and seduce me?' she asked huskily. 'That's not an armed truce, Jean-Marc.'

'But you did give me an unconditional surrender,' he reminded her, his mouth hard. 'And I accepted it without forcing you to live up to it. Surely in those circumstances you could come with me on this trip?'

A shiver ran through her. 'If I went abroad with you for three weeks, Jean-Marc, I would be without defence.'

His face lit suddenly with a smile so charming that it took her breath away as he leaned closer and kissed her mouth. 'That's the nicest thing you've ever said to me, *chérie*.'

Alicia's heart stopped beating, and when he drew away she said huskily, 'I know what you're asking me, Jean-Marc. I know what this war is being fought for.'

'Oh?' His dark brows rose as he studied her.

'You want me to be your mistress,' she said bitterly, dark eyes flashing. 'And that's a surrender I'll never give!'

His eyes narrowed on her face. Brutally, he said, 'We'll see about that, Alicia!' and then suddenly slid away, standing up, thrusting his hands in the pockets of that power suit, every inch the chairman of the board, the multi-millionaire tycoon with that hard, ruthless face and the determination in those steely, narrowed eyes. 'While I'm away, I expect you to carry on with your work, both here and in London.'

'Oh, do you?' she said angrily, sitting up, dragging her wrap back into a semblance of respectability, her hair love-tousled in a cloud around her slim shoulders, her mouth bruised with his kisses and her eyes flaming pools of dark gypsy passion. 'Well, just you remember that this is my decision! My choice! And it has been all the way down the line!'

'Well, quite!' he drawled softly, lifting dark arrogant brows.

Her face flamed. 'Very clever, Jean-Marc! You're trying to imply that I took this job because I wanted you! But that's about what I would expect from an arrogant, conceited——'

'I know you hate me, darling!' he drawled coolly, eyes mocking. 'But try to miss me while I'm away!' He bent his dark head, kissed her mouth before she could pull away, and studied her oddly before saying, 'I'll miss you.' Then he turned and strode to the door, opening it.

Alicia leapt off the bed, eyes blazing and ran to him, stopping him in the open doorway. 'I took this job because it was a superb opportunity!' she said fiercely. 'But you're making it too personal! While you're away, Jean-Marc, I shall continue to see myself as a free woman—and, if I wish to exercise my power of choice, I shall!'

His grey eyes flashed with sudden fury and he caught her arm, biting out, 'You'll take another man? Is that what you're saying, Alicia?'

'I was talking about my power of choice in life!' she said shakily, staring up at his hard, angry face with a thudding heart. 'But if that includes finding a new boyfriend, then that again is my prerogative!'

'No, it damned well isn't!' he said thickly, his mouth suddenly white. 'You're mine, Alicia, and I won't have another man coming near you! Is that understood?'

She was furious, dark eyes flaming. 'But you feel free to amuse yourself with Isabelle Janvier!'

'Leave her out of this!' he bit out forcefully. 'If I come back to find you've become involved with another man, I'll——' He broke off suddenly, his grey eyes flashing to a movement at the end of the corridor.

Alicia turned, saw Dominique standing there staring at them with round eyes, and realised what she must think, her face flooding with hot colour and her eyes closing in appalled bitter fury.

Dominique walked slowly into her bedroom and closed the door.

'Oh, God...!' Alicia said hoarsely, eyes flickering open to stare in accusation at Jean-Marc. 'She'll think I'm already your mistress!'

He looked at her, his eyes flint-like. 'Does that upset you, Alicia?'

'Of course it upsets me!' she flared, hating him bitterly. 'It makes me feel cheap and tacky! What on earth do you expect? You're the Last of the Great French Lovers and she's known you all your legendary life! To her, I'll just look like the latest in a long line of foolish women who fell for your legendary sex appeal!'

'Is that what you think lies between us, Alicia?' he asked grimly, and released her arm, his face hard. 'Perhaps it's best that I'm going away for three weeks. It will give you time to reflect on my actions.'

'I don't need to reflect on them!' she said shakily. 'I'm more than familiar with your technique!'

His eyes flashed with sudden grey fire. 'If I'd wanted you as my mistress,' he bit out under his breath, 'I could have had you by now!'

Her breath caught. 'You conceited swine!'

'You wouldn't have stopped me, Alicia!' he said tightly. 'You have been mine to take for a long time! Reflect on that while I am away!'

'What makes you so sure I'll still be here when you get back?'

He studied her, his mouth hard. 'If you are not, I will come and get you, and then, Alicia, I will show you no mercy.' Turning on his heel, he strode down the corridor, leaving her staring after him, shaking with bitter fury.

CHAPTER EIGHT

ALICIA settled into a routine fairly quickly. Every Friday she flew to Paris and was driven to the château. She would have a brief, friendly conversation with the chauffeur, and greet the butler by name on arrival, then go straight to her room. Dominique was always there, and she became a friend as well as a colleague. Sometimes, Pierre Dusort dropped by for a visit, and Alicia frequently dined with him and Dominique. Olivier was also a frequent visitor, spiriting Dominique off to drive in his red sports car to the town, where they sat in moody café-bars and talked teenage love-talk while listening to the jukebox.

During the week, Alicia lived and worked in London as normal. Only it didn't feel normal any more. By the time she left for Paris at the end of the third week, she found herself thinking of it as 'going home' for the weekend.

The wedding invitations had been sent out weeks ago, and Lindy had received one. Alicia was deeply relieved. Lindy had been deliberately ignoring her since their argument, and when she received her invitation she rang Alicia to tell her, and ask her for lunch.

It was something of a reconciliation between Alicia and her niece, but it was far from complete, and she was aware of Lindy's deep discomfort and

135

confusion as they ate at a smart restaurant in Sloane Square.

'So you really are working for him now?' Lindy asked with a flare of dark envy in her eyes. 'Mummy told me, of course, but I couldn't believe it until I read it in the Press.'

'Yes,' Alicia said huskily. 'I've had to give quite a few interviews since the wedding was announced. They all want to find out what the dress is like!'

Lindy smiled faintly. 'Lucky Dominique. Getting married . . .' Her eyes flashed suddenly. 'Maybe I will be, too.'

Alicia looked at her sharply. 'Have you found a boyfriend, Lindy?'

'Yes,' Lindy said with a brief, genuine smile. 'A nice boy called Phil. He works at Daddy's office in Richmond. I see him a lot.'

'That's wonderful!' Alicia said, eyes tracing her vulnerable face with love.

'Yes. A shame I can't take him to the wedding. Do you think I should go?' Lindy asked anxiously.

'Of course you should go!' Alicia said at once. 'Dominique and Olivier want you there.'

'And Jean-Marc?' Lindy asked with a trace of bitterness.

'Jean-Marc too,' Alicia assured her.

Lindy was unconvinced. 'Well, I'll accept the invitation for Dominique's sake. But I can't forget what Jean-Marc did, and I certainly can't forgive it.'

'Darling,' Alicia said gently, 'you must forgive him. If you don't, you'll keep those feelings alive, and they'll colour your life.' She heard herself saying those words and caught herself short. That's what I did, she thought in sudden shock. I kept my feelings for Tony alive, and they really have coloured my whole life.

'*How* can I forgive him?' Lindy said in agony.

'It isn't easy,' Alicia said slowly, 'and it can't be willed. One day you'll just turn a corner and find forgiveness there, waiting for you.'

Later, as she flew to Paris, Alicia thought of that conversation and saw it as the turning point it was. Somehow, somewhere along the line, she had forgiven Tony for what he had done to her when she was seventeen.

Tony... she thought, staring out of the limousine window later at the dark sky. He seemed so far away now. So vague, so harmless, so much a figure of the past.

The gates of Château Brissac swung open.

'*Bonsoir*, Mademoiselle Alicia!' the armed guard on the gate called.

'*Bonsoir*, Georges!' Alicia called back and waved, smiling.

They all knew her, now. All the kitchen staff, the housekeeping staff, the gardeners, the guards, the chauffeur and the aeroplane staff. Alicia had become a regular fixture in their lives, and they in hers.

The turrets of the château seemed to call a greeting as the limousine swung to a halt in front of it. Alicia got out, walked up to the steps, called a cheerful greeting in French to Etienne, the butler, and went straight to her room to unpack.

'Jean-Marc rang again today,' Dominique told her over dinner that night. 'We had a wonderful gossip!'

Alicia's pulse raced at the mention of his name. 'What did he say?'

'The trip is going well.' Dominique sipped her onion soup. 'He's had to fire a few people and promote some others, but everything's running smoothly again in Tokyo and Sydney, and he's flying to New York tonight.'

'Busy man,' Alicia said, hurt that he had not contacted her since he had gone. It was weeks now, and not even a postcard.

'He asked after you,' Dominique said, making her heart skip beats, 'as he always does. He wanted to know if you'd arrived and I said you had.'

'He rang while I was here?' Alicia asked, eyes widening. 'Didn't—I mean, didn't he want to speak to me?'

'No.' Dominique eyed her curiously. 'I assumed you spoke to him regularly. I thought——' She broke off, flushing.

Alicia flushed too, and bent her head to her soup, quickly changing the subject. Jean-Marc only wanted to know if she was here. That hurt, and she hated him for not contacting her, although she knew it was irrational considering the fact that she *did* hate him.

Next morning, Dominique burst into the office at nine o'clock.

'Guess what!' she trilled in French, dark eyes flashing.

'What . . . ?' Alicia looked up from the design painting of the ballroom she was working on.

Dominique ushered Etienne in with a vast bouquet of flowers. 'I bet I know who they're from!'

Alicia gasped, staring at the enormous bouquet. Her hands shook as she ripped the envelope and read the card:

'Tu es mienne—Jean-Marc.'

A shiver went through her. She stared at the card, the words burning into her mind. 'You're mine . . .' She thought of what he had said when he left—that he would come after her if she wasn't there, and show her no mercy. The thought of him showing her no mercy was enough to bring a deep gnawing excitement to the pit of her stomach, so deep that it was agony. And the fact that she had stayed told Jean-Marc how she felt.

'Isn't he gorgeous?' Dominique said, fluttering around the flowers while Etienne watched indulgently. 'And look at these roses . . . !'

'Shall I put them in water, Mademoiselle Alicia?' Etienne asked.

'Thank you,' she said huskily, and propped the card on her desk.

The weekend sped by. Alicia got through a lot of work. By the time she flew back to London, she felt she had broken the back of the wedding arrangements. Ballatria was already making up the bridal gown and the four bridesmaids' dresses. Pageboy outfits had been designed, and were waiting to be cut. The ballroom was now under attack, as Jean-Marc would have put it, and after this weekend's work on the décor Alicia was certain everything would be ready in time.

Back in London, life at her offices was doubly hectic. A collection was being put into operation, and she worked herself into exhaustion, but it was an exhilarating achievement to keep it all under control.

On Friday, Alicia had lunch with Susannah in Richmond.

'It all sounds terribly glam and exciting!' Susannah smiled with interest when Alicia finished telling her about her current lifestyle. 'Much more your kind of thing than mine, though.'

Alicia smiled, studying her contented face. 'You don't even like flying, do you?'

Susannah crossed herself. 'No, I don't! But I like to hear you talk about it. You've always lived life in the fast lane, haven't you? You have a taste for action, excitement and power.'

'Do I?' Alicia stared at the late summer sun on the river, thinking of Jean-Marc and how apt that description would be of him.

'Yes.' Susannah smiled. 'But I don't. I'm happy with my lazy, carefree life. I wouldn't swap it for all the glamour in the world.'

Alicia walked back to her car later, thinking about her sister's words. The long red Jaguar XJS convertible was parked in a leafy street, and as Alicia looked up she saw a gold leaf on a tree and realised autumn was on its way, filtering into life gradually, changing the season in secret, no one noticing its approach until it was too late.

Just like Jean-Marc Brissac, she thought, and realised with a shock how much he had changed her life.

'Alicia?' a male voice said close by, and she turned, frowning to see David standing watching her on the pavement.

'David!' She stared at him as though he was a stranger.

He gave a faint smile, a flush on his smooth face. 'How are you?'

She nodded slowly. 'I'm fine. And you?'

'Oh, I'm OK,' he shrugged, eyes flicking over her, taking in the smart dove-grey mini-suit she wore teamed with a rich pink silk blouse. 'You look stunning as ever! I hear you're working for Brissac now?'

'I've been working for him for a month,' she said quietly. 'And I hear you're seeing Eileen again?'

'Yes...' He smiled, gave a sheepish laugh. 'I guess I loved her all along. And she took me back—once she'd beaten me over the head with a verbal saucepan.'

Alicia nodded. 'She's a lovely girl. I can't think why you split with her in the first place.'

David said nothing, studying her, then said lightly, 'I like your hair like that. It suits you better than the chignon.'

'Oh...' Alicia ran a hand through her long, loose black hair. She always wore it loose now. It had become a habit, and it suited her, emphasised the beauty of her high cheekbones and dark gypsy eyes. 'Yes, I changed the style...maybe because my life changed so suddenly.'

'Mine too,' he said with a smile.

They met each other's eyes in a moment of forgiveness, and Alicia suddenly realised they had nothing more to say to each other.

'Well...' David shifted uncomfortably, hands in pockets. 'I guess I'd better be going. I just had lunch with Eileen. I'm late for work...'

Alicia smiled, said quietly, 'Goodbye, David.'

'Bye.' He waved a hand, walked away without a backward glance.

Alicia watched him go, her dark eyes thoughtful. They had been like strangers. It was almost impossible to believe they had ever been a couple, ever planned to marry. As she got into her red XJS, she glanced in her rear-view mirror and saw David disappear around the corner. As simple as that, she thought, staring. As simple as that...

When she arrived at the château that weekend, Pierre Dusort was there and an awful racket of loud pop music was coming from the drawing-room. Alicia went to her room and unpacked as usual, then went down to investigate.

Olivier and Dominique were dancing like wild things, bouncing up and down in rhythm to the music, their faces zombie-like and their clothes quite frighteningly trendy.

'Could you turn it down a bit?' Alicia shouted in French above the blasting beat, feeling suddenly old.

Dominique looked up, face flushed and excited. 'Oh, God, you're worse than Jean-Marc!' she groaned, and obediently went to the compact disc player to switch it off. 'What an old wrinkly you're turning into!'

Alicia made a face. 'It was just so loud...'

'My daughter sometimes makes me feel,' drawled Pierre Dusort appearing behind her in the doorway, 'that she is not yet old enough to marry!'

'Oh, yes, I am!' Dominique said and flounced over to Olivier, catching him by the lapels and pulling him towards her for a passionate kiss.

'Dominique!' Alicia gasped, shocked.

Pierre laughed, studying her face and drawled, 'She is French, Alicia. And that makes her free to express her passions!'

Alicia looked up at him with sudden self-consciousness, thinking of Jean-Marc and everything he had said to her so forcefully about her capacity to express passion.

'We're going out on the town!' Dominique announced, leading Olivier behind her by his tie. 'To see and be seen! To kiss and be kissed! To love and make love!'

'Not in this town, young lady!' Pierre said flatly, arching dark brows. 'You behave yourself. And don't hang around with those rebels! You know it will only get into the papers!'

Dominique rolled her eyes at Alicia. 'Just because I was photographed on the back of a boy's motorbike last year!' She kissed her father. 'I'll behave! I promise! Goodnight!'

When they had gone, Pierre turned to Alicia. 'That leaves us alone for the evening. The unpaid cabaret have gone.'

Alicia smiled. 'I'll get some work done.'

'You work too hard.' Pierre frowned. 'Even if Jean-Marc is paying you a king's ransom. Come out to dinner tonight with me. I'm not a workaholic. I'm a dilettante and I would enjoy some unashamed laziness!'

Alicia agreed on impulse, and they drove in Pierre's limousine to the best restaurant in the town of Brissac, two kilometres away.

It was an enjoyable evening of unashamed relaxation. The restaurant had a lazy, bohemian atmosphere with candles and checked tablecloths, but the food was cordon bleu. Alicia ate chilled *crevettes* followed by marvellous *truite aux amandes*.

'Jean-Marc has always been as dynamic as he is now,' Pierre told her as they ate. 'He totally changed the Brissac banking house. When his father had a heart attack and retired, Jean-Marc took over and put a rocket under it.'

'It wasn't always international?' she asked, surprised.

'No. Jean-Marc made it the vast international concern it is today. He expanded at a rate of knots. Hong Kong, New York, Sydney——'

'Tokyo,' Alicia supplied, a proud smile in her eyes as she thought of him. 'Is it true there's a Brissac bank in every capital of the world?'

'And every state of America.' Pierre agreed, smiling, 'Yes, he's quite a guy, isn't he? I'm nothing like him. Chalk and cheese. I inherited my money, and never really did anything with it. He inherited his, too, but look what he did with it!'

'You're very close, though,' Alicia said, studying his face.

'Very.' Pierre nodded. 'I admire him, and I like to think he admires me. Certainly, he is my closest friend. He was wonderful when my wife died a few years ago. I don't know what I'd have done without him. And he obviously adores my daughter.'

It was late when they drove home. Alicia asked Pierre to take them by the scenic route. Although she had been out shopping several times in Brissac, she had not seen much of the surrounding countryside. At night, it was very beautiful, and

Pierre got carried away with the drive, going a little too far out.

They got back to Château Brissac at one o'clock in the morning.

'I'll never get up in the morning for work!' Alicia groaned, getting out of the car.

Pierre laughed ruefully, putting a friendly arm around her. 'You'll manage. You always do. You and Jean-Marc . . . so much alike.'

Alicia wished him goodnight and went straight up to her bedroom. She was smiling as she opened the door, but when she saw the bedside lamp on, she caught her breath, staring as Jean-Marc stood up slowly from the bed.

There was a long, tense silence while they stared at each other.

'Jean-Marc,' she said unsteadily, 'when did you get back?'

'Tonight,' he said under his breath. 'At nine o'clock.'

'Oh . . .' Her heart was thudding painfully. He looked so gorgeous, his black V-neck sweater and black trousers emphasising his muscular power and tremendous sex appeal.

'I had planned to surprise you,' he said grimly. 'But it seems I was the one who got the surprise.'

'What do you mean?' she asked, hand sweating on the door-handle as she stood there, poised for flight, suddenly sensing the anger beneath his frightening calm.

He gave a hard, cynical smile. 'I come home to find you are out with another man, Alicia. So I wait, to see when you will come home. And now it is fifteen minutes past one.' The rage behind those silver eyes was making her pulses leap with alarm. 'I wonder just what you were doing until this time in the morning.'

'We went for a drive,' she said carefully.

He gave a harsh laugh and walked towards her, very controlled. 'Oh, yes? What kind of drive? Did you stop, Alicia? Did you pull over in a lovers' lay-by and——?'

'Don't be ridiculous!' she said angrily, face flaming. 'I was with Pierre! Pierre Dusort—what on earth do you think——?'

'My best friend!' he said hoarsely, his mouth white. 'You really know where to stick the knife, Alicia! You could have chosen any man! But you chose Pierre!'

'Don't shout at me!' she said fiercely, wrenching the door open to try and escape.

'Come back, you little *salope*!' he bit out shakingly, seizing her by the scruff of the neck, dragging her back in, slamming the door and pushing her hard against it, his eyes blazing. 'You knew exactly how to hit me hardest, didn't you? How long has it been going on? How many times have you seen him?'

'I haven't been seeing him!' she said angrily, struggling against the biting grip of his hard hands as he pinned her to the door. 'Ask him if you don't believe me!'

'I can't!' he said thickly, his eyes silver with rage. 'He knows nothing about us! He's not involved, Alicia! If he asked you out it was because he didn't know you were mine! He would never have betrayed me knowingly. Never...'

'He didn't betray you now, Jean-Marc!' she said huskily, staring into his hellish eyes. 'It was just coincidence. Dominique and Olivier went out. Pierre was bored. He suggested dinner...' She blurted it all out in a hot rush. 'I accepted and we went.'

He was breathing hoarsely, his eyes intent. 'How can I believe that? You only got back five minutes ago!'

'I told you,' she said, feeling sick with tension, 'he took me for a drive. I wanted to see the countryside.'

He stared at her for a long moment, then said roughly, 'He didn't kiss you?'

Mute, she shook her head.

Jean-Marc stared at her, breathing hard. 'Did you want him to kiss you, Alicia?'

'No,' she said, her heart drumming, 'it didn't occur to me.'

His strong hands left her wrists, framed her face. 'Prove it!'

Her heart skipped a beat. Her eyes drowned in his. 'What do you mean?'

'You know what I mean, Alicia,' he said thickly. 'You've told me your story, and now I want you to prove it. All of it. Every last word.'

'How?' she asked, though she knew.

His mouth tightened into a white line and he bit out under his breath, 'Surrender to me! Now! Give me everything I need to ease my pain and anger!'

She caught her breath, sudden anger flashing in her dark eyes. 'I've told you the truth! What more do you want?'

'I've spent the last four hours sitting up here waiting for you to come home from your date with my best friend!' he said hoarsely. 'And I'm eaten up with tension! Now I want you to prove you didn't try to test your new-found passion on Pierre—or any other man—in my absence!'

'But how can I prove that?'

He gave a harsh laugh. 'How do you think?' His eyes moved insultingly over her body and his hand shot suddenly to her breast, stroking it, his fingers hard. 'If you let me take you, I'll soon find out if you've been unfaithful!'

Her hand slapped him hard across the face and his head jerked back.

With a snarl, he scooped her up into his arms, carried her struggling body to the bed, laid her down on it and joined her, ignoring her angry fight, taking her wrists and pinning them to the mattress as his long hard body took dominance.

'Please...!' she whispered as his head blotted out the light. 'Jean-Marc, don't...!'

His hard mouth closed over hers, silencing her, and at once the desire flooded through her, her long hoarse moan as she opened her mouth to him making his hands shake as they slid away from her wrists to the hips, and she found herself sliding against him, her hands moving instinctively to his strong neck, his thick black hair, pushing through it with restless movements.

The kiss deepened, and she was lost in a sensual daze, her mouth hungrily passionate on his, her body warm and responsive as his strong hands ran over it, both impatient to kiss and to touch each other after such a long absence.

Like the lovers they had gradually become, they became inflamed so quickly that Alicia's hoarse moans mingled with Jean-Marc's rough sounds of excitement, and his hands grew impatient with the exquisite red silk dress she wore, stroking the zip down, pulling the dress over her shoulders, revealing the lacy red bra she wore.

'*Mon Dieu...!*' he muttered thickly, tugging the red lace bra down to expose her full breasts and the erect pink nipples that throbbed for his touch. 'Alicia...tell me you thought of me when I was away! Tell me you thought of this!'

'Yes...!' she whispered, and he bent his dark head with a groan, his hot mouth closing over her nipple, eliciting a hoarse cry of excitement from her as she arched towards him, her hands in his hair.

His mouth sucked hungrily at her breast, his strong hands stroking her slim thighs as she moved against him, and he raised his head, thrust one strong thigh between hers, moved back to take her mouth, kissing her deeply.

'I thought of you constantly!' he said thickly against her mouth. 'You're a drug in my bloodstream!'

'You didn't call!' she whispered accusingly. 'You didn't write! Three weeks, and not even a postcard!' Her voice shook with bitterness.

'I sent you flowers!' he said harshly, raising his dark head, face deeply flushed and eyes glittering with fever. 'What more did you want?'

Her mouth quivered with deep passion. 'You're such a practised lover! How many women have you sent flowers to? And how personal is it? Just a phone call and a credit-card number!'

'You would have argued with me if I had called you,' he said sardonically. 'And you would have read any written communication with suspicion.'

She flushed, lowering her lashes. What he said was true.

He watched her in silence for a moment, then said deeply, 'Did it hurt, Alicia? To no longer be the centre of my universe?'

With a gasp, she looked up at him.

'Is that why you went out with my best friend?' he asked grimly. 'To get back at me?'

'I told you!' she said angrily. 'Pierre was bored and——'

'And you knew it would hurt me,' he said thickly, his hands tightening on her waist. 'Which is exactly why you did it. Don't deny it, Alicia. I see it in your eyes, a flash of triumph, even though I know you dare not admit it to yourself.'

Hot colour swept her face. 'I didn't do it deliberately! I didn't even know you were back, or that you'd find out!'

'I don't doubt you never admitted it consciously to yourself,' he said tightly. 'But you knew I'd find out. And you knew, when I did, I would be jealous.'

Her breath caught and she said bitterly, 'Just as I was jealous when I caught you with Isabelle!'

He stared for a second, then laughed softly, and as he did she realised how she had betrayed her deepest motives in going out with Pierre tonight, and knew he was right: she had done it deliberately, unconsciously, needing badly to get back at him and thrust the knife of jealousy into his heart.

'Oh...!' she whispered in appalled self-awareness. 'Oh, no...!'

'Oh, yes,' he said thickly. 'You were seething inside and you wanted to make me seethe. Well, you got your wish, Alicia. I am burning with jealousy and rage.' He moved away from her, tore his black sweater off, muscles rippling as his tanned flesh was exposed. 'Here...' he said thickly, touching the left side of his chest.

With a breathless moan, she was sliding her hands to his broad shoulders, her mouth opening against his chest, luxuriating in his harsh muffled sound of excitement, the fierce ragged heartbeat against her face and the feel of that taut flesh, the black hairs and warmth.

'You stuck a knife through my heart!' Jean-Marc said thickly, pulling her face back up, his hard mouth very close. 'You betray yourself, she-devil!' His hand slid to her bare breast, felt the thudding heartbeat. 'You betray your desire...!'

His mouth closed over hers again, and they went up in flames, their hands running over each other with hoarse cries of need, and when he gave a low snarl and began to tug the red silk dress from her she barely noticed, lost in the fire of his mouth, her eyes closed and her head spinning as he stripped her to her red lace briefs.

He was breathing harshly, pressing her semi-nude body against his, and the male hardness burned a dominant need against her centre as he parted her slender legs, one strong hand shaking on her inner thigh, his mouth sliding over hers with the possession she had needed for so long.

When his strong hands properly unhooked the bra, she started to pant, shivering with hot excitement as he dropped it to the floor and ran his hands over her, making her moan, her jaw locked with intolerable tension as she moved helplessly, rhythmically against his hardness, hardly knowing what she was doing, her eyes closed and her head thrown back in an agony of need.

Jean-Marc muttered something hoarsely under his breath, lifting his dark head from her, staring down at her as though about to go insane, his breath coming fast and his heart slamming against his chest.

Suddenly, he closed his eyes and moved away from her, swinging off the bed, raking a hand through his thick black hair and staring down at her, his grey eyes flickering with restless hunger over her long-limbed, passionately sensual face and body.

'I want you to move in here with me,' he said thickly. 'Leave your London house and come here for good.'

Her eyes widened in horror. 'What...?'

'I can't go on like this,' he said under his breath. 'Seeing you only at weekends, in between business trips——'

'You mean you want me to become your mistress!' she said hoarsely, sitting up in bed, suddenly covered in deep shame and humiliation as she dragged the silk quilt up over her nudity.

'Don't be absurd,' he said thickly. 'You are still seconds away from becoming my mistress, Alicia! I could have taken you just now and you would have welcomed it!'

She winced, bitterly ashamed. 'You bastard!'

He gave an angry laugh. 'How can I be a bastard when I did not take what you so obviously wanted to give me?'

Alicia lowered her eyes, mouth white as she plucked at the silk duvet, hating him for telling the truth, hating herself for being such a fool, so easily drowned in sensual fire by his kisses.

'*Chérie,*' Jean-Marc studied her bent head, his voice roughening, 'I want you with me. That is all. And besides—you are scheduled to move in in two weeks' time to put the wedding plans into full operation.'

'That's different,' she said huskily. 'It's business.'

He laughed under his breath, sank down on to the bed beside her. 'Alicia, I want you with me.' His hand slid under her chin, forced her face up. 'And if you're honest, you will admit you feel the same.'

She looked at him through her lashes, her face flushed.

'You did miss me,' he said softly, 'didn't you?'

Her eyes closed. 'Yes...!' she whispered bitterly.

A smile touched the hard mouth. 'Then do as I ask. When you fly back to London, pack as many things as possible and move in for the month preceding the wedding.'

'Making it clear to the entire world that I'm your mistress?' she asked angrily, flashing her eyes open, filled with dark hate. 'I'd rather die, Jean-Marc!'

His mouth tightened. 'I want you with me!' he bit out under his breath, then stood up again, his eyes angry, scooped up his black sweater and strode to the door, biting out over one shoulder, 'And I will have you!'

The door slammed so hard as he left that the wood rattled.

CHAPTER NINE

OF COURSE, Alicia was now face to face with her own folly. Jean-Marc had been pushing her towards this choice from the moment he came into her room at the Ritz and forced her to respond to his kiss. She wanted him, and he had known it from the very beginning. And what was the very beginning? If she was honest, it was the moment she first saw him, first met those grey eyes across the room with Lindy beside her, and felt that rage flash out of her like an electric current. Her passionate involvement with him had started with that moment, and led to this one: her sitting almost naked on a bed, her hair tousled, her eyes burning, and her mouth bruised with his kiss.

It's not love, though, she thought with pain stinging her heart. He doesn't love me. He just wants to make me his mistress, and, after a long hard fight, he's almost got me there: where I wanted to be all along.

But it wasn't what she wanted. Or at least, it wasn't enough. She knew that as she sat there, staring into space with hurt eyes, and feeling the empty ache in her heart.

Of course she was in love with him.

Hopelessly in love with him, and that really was the deciding factor. Alicia had always prided herself on being so cool, calm, collected. So successful and sophisticated and together, with her streamlined life under total control.

The truth was, that had always been a front for her wildly romantic heart, for her vulnerability and chaotic emotions, and the danger she knew awaited her if she ever let her guard down.

Well, she had let her guard down with Jean-Marc Brissac, and now she was going to have to pay the price. She had no choice now. No choice at all.

Slowly, she got to her feet, her legs shaking, and began to dress. It was two o'clock in the morning, but she knew a taxi would come if she rang for one, and by the time she reached Paris an early morning flight would be ready to take her back to London.

It was like killing herself to walk out of the château gates at three in the morning when the taxi slowly sidled up. The engine ran and the headlights blazed in the cool darkness, and the driver looked at her curiously as she got in, but she couldn't speak, and a moment later she was on her way home.

Her flight landed at eight a.m. at Heathrow, and she shivered as she caught a black taxi to Chelsea. Her house seemed to echo with her own heartbreak, but she forced herself to lock up properly, take the phone off the hook.

Then, Alicia went to bed and cried herself to sleep.

It was six o'clock at night when she awoke. The house smelt of loneliness and heartbreak. She couldn't stay here. Besides, it would be the first place Jean-Marc would look for her.

Half an hour later, she got into her red XJS and drove to Richmond.

'Alicia!' Susannah's face was a picture of shock as she opened the front door. 'What on earth are you doing here? I thought you were in France with——'

'I had to leave,' Alicia said, her eyes blazing with dark emotion. 'I couldn't think of anywhere else to go, so I came here. Am I intruding?'

'No, not at all!' Susannah held the door wide, staring at Alicia's white face, bruised mouth and the tousled silk of her long dark hair. 'I was just making moussaka for Bobby. He's still at the pub, though, and Lindy's out with this new boyfriend of hers. Come in . . .'

Alicia went in, going immediately to the warm well-lit kitchen, the sound of the television blaring from the living-room. For a second, she just stood in the kitchen, her mouth trembling with the need to talk.

Susannah studied her with a concerned frown. 'What's wrong, Alicia?' she asked gently. 'You look as though you've been through the mill.'

Alicia's dark eyes shimmered with tears as she raised them to her sister's face. 'Oh, Susannah,' she said rawly, 'I think I've fallen in love with him.'

Susannah caught her breath, walking to her and catching her in a warm embrace. Alicia burst into tears on her plump shoulder for the first time since she was a small child, and found herself clinging to her, unable to stem the flow of tears.

It occurred to her as she cried that she had not cried when her parents died. It also occurred to her that that had been a bad idea. But all the emotion was whirling inside of her, pouring out as she clung to her sister, crying uncontrollably.

'There now,' Susannah said gently when at last the storm of weeping was over, and drew back to study Alicia's ravaged face. 'You really needed that, didn't you?'

Alicia nodded, groping for a tissue, and blew her nose.

'I take it you mean Jean-Marc Brissac?' Susannah watched her with understanding eyes. 'You're in love with him?'

Alicia nodded, screwing up the tissue, and the television continued to blare incessantly in the other room.

'Tell me what happened,' Susannah said, 'while I make you a nice cup of tea.'

Brokenly, Alicia began to tell her, leaving out the more intimate details and the more betraying revelations of her own passionate nature, but letting Susannah see that Jean-Marc had tried to coerce her into becoming his mistress.

'It doesn't surprise me,' Susannah said later, sipping her tea with a wry smile. 'I knew it would happen once I heard you'd been caught in a sizzling clinch with him!'

Alicia stared. 'A sizzling clinch...!'

'Well, that's what it was, wasn't it?' Susannah laughed. 'And as soon as I heard that I thought: this is it. She's met him.'

'Susannah...' Alicia said slowly '...I don't think you understand what's happened to me!'

'Oh, yes, I do,' Susannah said gently. 'You've fallen in love, and this is what love is like, Alicia. It's not a streamlined business operation. It's not something you can control like your career. Love is something much more living than that. It's like two wild animals, recognising each other and deciding to mate.'

'Susannah!' Alicia gasped, shocked.

'But it's got to be the right animal,' Susannah continued, smiling. 'And you're a lioness, Alicia. You weren't going to fall in love until a lion came along and roared at you.'

Alicia gaped, her mouth opening and closing in stunned silence.

'Jean-Marc Brissac is perfect for you,' Susannah went on, amused by her young sister's shock. 'I haven't met him yet, of course, but I can tell he's the one. He's like you—isn't he? He's devastatingly attractive, he's got lethal sex appeal, a taste for power, excitement, adventure and ambition—and he's ready to settle down.' She tapped her teacup with one unpolished fingernail. 'Perfect!'

'But he wants me to be his mistress!' Alicia said fiercely.

'Well, he would say that, wouldn't he?' Susannah drawled. 'He's much too proud and much too masculine to tell you he's in love with you.'

Alicia's eyes darted. Her breath quickened. 'He can't be in love with me...' she whispered. 'Not *me*!'

'I expect he thinks the same about you,' Susannah said softly.

Alicia stared, said shakily, 'But he's so fantastic...he's got everything... What on earth would he see in me?'

Susannah laughed, dark eyes dancing. 'Alicia, he's moved mountains to get you! Why else would he do it, if not because he loves you?'

She felt her eyes stare fixedly at her sister's face. Those words revolved in her brain, but she couldn't let herself believe it, couldn't bear to be such a fool, couldn't tolerate the fear of emotional pain that had been such a constant threat to her for so many years, and which Jean-Marc Brissac had been breaking down, bit by bit, step by passionate step, until at last she had fallen in a landslide of love, not recognising her own powerful feelings until it was too late.

Suddenly, the television sound was piercing her mind. A man was reading the news headlines and she heard the words with a sense of horror and unreality.

'Dominique Dusort,' said the television newscaster's voice, 'the goddaughter of the French multi-millionaire, Jean-Marc Brissac, was kidnapped in the early hours of this morning in her home town of Brissac——'

'Oh, my God!' Susannah said grimly, and got up.

The colour drained from Alicia's face as she rushed into the living-room, shaking, staring at the photograph of Jean-Marc and hearing the newscaster saying,

'Monsieur Brissac contacted the police immediately he received the ransom demand. He later flew by helicopter to Paris to meet with the Sûreté. Our correspondent, John Beaver, reports...'

The picture switched to a film report. There was the flash of a limousine surrounded by jostling reporters. Then Jean-Marc stepping out of the expensive car, shouldering through them, his face grim with tension and his mouth a hard white line.

Alicia sank into a chair, her legs too weak to hold her.

'You must go to him, Alicia,' Susannah said, as Jean-Marc's helicopter was shown landing at Château Brissac this evening, accompanied by two police helicopters. 'If he is in love with you, he'll be absolutely devastated that you've left him now.'

'Yes...' she said shakily, getting to her feet, walking unsteadily to the kitchen, getting her bag and keys. 'Poor Dominique...what if they hurt her? Oh, God, I couldn't bear it!'

'Just pray.' Susannah walked her to the front door. 'And get to Jean-Marc immediately. Want me to ring the airport and book your flight?'

Alicia turned, white-faced and filled with fear. 'Please. And could you book a car to meet me and drive me back to the château?'

'I'll do both right away.' Susannah nodded, opened the front door, and on impulse flung her arms around Alicia, holding her close in a moment of shared anxiety. 'Take care, love!' she whispered. 'And it's lovely to have you back again. You've been so lonely for so long, haven't you?'

Alicia's dark eyes filled with hot tears. 'Yes...' she admitted at last, and disappeared into the red XJS a moment later, wiping tears from her pale cheeks as she drove home, flung her suitcase back together again, and then roared along the motorway at high speed to Heathrow.

Reporters were jostling at the gates of Château Brissac as her taxi pulled up. It was midnight. Alicia called to Georges, the gate-guard, and the electronic buzz swung the gates wide. Flashbulbs exploded in the night as the taxi sped on to the drive to the château itself. Police cars and vans were parked outside the front door.

'*Mademoiselle!*' Etienne was grey-faced with anxiety as he met her in the hall. 'Thank God you returned!'

'Where is he, Etienne?' she asked huskily as the chauffeur carried her suitcase upstairs.

'In the study with the police.' Etienne led the way. 'They've been here all night, waiting for the next communication. Oh, *mademoiselle*, we're all so frantic...!'

Alicia put a comforting hand on the old butler's shoulder. 'Try not to worry too much. I'm sure Dominique will come to no harm.'

The study had a tense atmosphere when she went in. A tape machine was set up by the telephone. Plain-clothes detectives sat talking to Jean-Marc at the desk, and Jean-Marc himself looked hellish. Pierre Dusort sat on a long dark leather sofa, his head in his hands.

Jean-Marc looked up when she came in, and his eyes widened. His face was taut with strain, his mouth white and his grey eyes shadowed from lack of sleep. His black jacket hung over the back of the chair, his black waistcoat unbuttoned to hang loose on his powerful frame, his red tie hanging in straight lines either side of his neck and his white shirt unbuttoned at the throat.

Alicia walked silently to his side, sinking down in the chair next to him. He met her dark gaze, and his black lashes flickered on his tough, tense cheekbones. But he said nothing, and as they looked at each other Alicia felt her mouth quiver with emotion.

A senior police officer in a smart black suit watched Alicia with interest. His blue gaze flicked to Jean-Marc's face and back to Alicia's as though figuring out what had happened between them.

Suddenly, the telephone rang.

Everyone tensed, staring at it.

'A call's come through. Get a trace on it,' the officer in the black suit said into a walkie-talkie, then motioned Jean-Marc to answer it. 'Just keep them talking.'

Jean-Marc snatched up the receiver. 'Brissac!'

Alicia watched the lines of strain deepen at his mouth as he listened. Her heart ached with love.

'Where is she?' Jean-Marc's curt voice asked in French. 'If you've hurt her...'

It was the kidnappers, then. Alicia listened, acute tension in her face, thinking of poor Dominique. Did they have Olivier, too? How had it happened? She watched Jean-Marc snatch up a black and silver pen and write something down in bold black handwriting.

'Don't be a fool!' Jean-Marc said suddenly, grey eyes flaring. 'Just because I told the police? What did you expect me to do? Yes, I know I agreed to your terms! You changed them—I followed suit!'

The officer in the black suit was motioning wildly for Jean-Marc to keep them on the line longer, not to argue with them.

'I can't possibly liquidate that much cash in twenty-four hours!' Jean-Marc said tightly, then sat forwards, face white. 'No! Wait——' His mouth tightened in the silence that followed, and he lowered the receiver, his eyes grim. 'He hung up.'

The officer spoke rapidly into his walkie-talkie. Machine-gun French burst back at him. Jean-Marc grimly replaced the receiver. The tape machine switched off.

'We have an area trace!' The officer looked up with sharp blue eyes. 'And it's France. Not far from here, in fact. The call came from St Aubin de Château.'

Jean-Marc sucked in his breath. 'Fifty kilometres away!'

'Yes. It seems you were right, Monsieur Brissac. The kidnappers are amateurs. Young rebels.' His eyes narrowed. 'I take it new demands were made just now?'

'The price doubled,' Jean-Marc said tensely. 'A hundred million francs.'

Sharp intakes of breath went around the officers, who all looked at each other, and the officer in chief pursed his hard mouth in a silent whistle.

'What else?'

'They want it delivered at midnight tomorrow night. The location is changed, though.' He tore off the piece of paper he had written on and handed it to the officer. 'A suitcase containing the money is to be lowered from a helicopter into the valley below Les Baux-de-Provence.'

'Clever,' the officer said, mouth twisting.

'They're learning fast,' Jean-Marc said grimly.

'But is Dominique all right?' Pierre Dusort asked hoarsely from the long couch, and he looked as though he had aged twenty years.

'So I was told.' Jean-Marc's face was ashen below his tan, his grey eyes bleak. He looked back at the officer. 'But there is no proof, Girot. We must find her fast.'

'I'll arrange a search of the area,' Girot said curtly, and got to his feet. 'You get the money.'

'A hundred million francs?' Jean-Marc said grimly. 'Cash? On a Sunday? At one in the morning?' He gave a harsh laugh, but picked up the telephone and began making calls.

He was successful. By two o'clock in the morning, he had the promise of the cash from a Swiss bank, to be flown by helicopter to the château, arriving at approximately midday tomorrow.

'I need a drink,' Jean-Marc said, standing up, 'and some fresh air. If you need anything to eat or drink, just ring the kitchens on the house phone. Number fourteen. Gentlemen . . .'

Girot turned, frowning. 'You must stay up, Monsieur Brissac. They could call back. We could find them. Anything could happen.'

'I won't be far,' he said grimly, and strode wearily to the door.

Alicia got up and followed him silently, closing the door behind her and watching him walk to the drawing-room, going in leaving the door open and picking up a whisky bottle from the drinks cabinet.

'You left me,' Jean-Marc said deeply, without turning, as though he sensed her presence so acutely that he did not need to reassure himself that she was behind him.

'Yes . . .' Alicia's eyes moved over his dark head with love, and she closed the door.

'But you came back.' He turned, a whisky glass in one hand, and his grey eyes were bleak. 'Because of the kidnapping?'

'I saw the story on the news in London.'

'And were afraid for Dominique.' His mouth firmed into a white line, he studied his whisky, then said, 'You must have grown very fond of her.'

Her heart twisted. 'Yes...' What else could she say? Declare her feelings for him and risk brutal rejection?

He raised the whisky glass to his hard mouth and drank.

'How did it all happen?' Alicia asked haltingly.

'Olivier and Dominique were at a bar in town,' he said flatly. 'They were asked to a party. They went. Olivier was heavily drugged by someone without his knowledge. He didn't know what had happened until he woke up in a ditch, alone. By the time he managed to walk to the nearest village and summon help, it was dawn. The ransom note had been sewn on to the back of his jacket. The police contacted me immediately.'

'Where is Olivier now?'

'Upstairs,' he said deeply, 'under sedation and watched by a nurse. He's recovering from shock. The police suspected him at first and interrogated him. I intervened in the end because I could see he was on the point of some kind of breakdown, and so could the police once I'd pointed it out.'

'You suspected him?' she asked slowly.

'Not really.' He made a grim face. 'But the police have a job to do, and I didn't want to flex too many muscles by interfering. I had to, in the end, but only to save Olivier's mental health.'

'What did the ransom note say?' she asked huskily, appalled for poor Olivier and the ordeal he had been through. As for Dominique...she couldn't bear to think of what she was still going through.

'"We have Dominique Dusort,"' he recited, running a tired hand over his eyes. '"Do not contact the police if you wish to see her alive again. We will telephone at ten o'clock with our demands. Answer the call personally or Dominique dies."'

Alicia winced. 'What made you contact the police?'

'The call didn't come,' he said flatly, and drained the whisky glass. 'And the Press already had the story. I was besieged by reporters by nine a.m.'

'Presumably, that's why the kidnappers didn't call,' Alicia said slowly.

'Yes. At midday, I flew to Paris to meet with Girot. I had no option by then.' He flexed his tired shoulder muscles, grimacing.

Alicia moved forwards, her dark eyes on his face. 'Let me...'

His eyes flickered open, watching her grimly, his mouth white. Slowly, Alicia moved to stand behind him, her hands on his shoulders beginning to massage the iron tension from them.

He gave a low, harsh groan. *'Chérie...'*

'Sit down,' she said huskily, her pulses leaping, and he moved silently to the couch, sinking on to it as she sank beside him and continued to un-knot those locked muscles.

Jean-Marc's eyes flicked to her face, and suddenly he shifted, lying face down on the couch, his arms stretched limply. Alicia moved to accommodate him, sitting beside his strong hips as she began to massage his back, unlocking the muscles along the spine, listening to his harsh groans of pleasure-pain and feeling the muscles relax slowly as she worked her way up his spine, kneading the muscles from left to right until she reached his hard shoulders again.

As she went to work on those shoulders he muttered something in French, his face in pained ecstasy, and she could feel the muscles locked tight, so she worked hard on them as he groaned, and eventually her fingers reached his strong neck and unlocked that, too.

His strong hand suddenly closed over hers, and he turned on to his back, staring up at her. 'Why did you leave, Alicia?' he asked deeply. 'Because I asked you to move in?'

She met his grey gaze, her pulses skipping. 'Yes.'

'You were going to move in soon, anyway,' he said, his face bleak. 'Why did you run from me just because I——?'

'Does it matter now?' she asked huskily, her heartbeat unsteady as she bravely ran a tender hand through his black hair. 'I'm here now, and I won't be leaving again.'

His eyes searched hers. 'You're here to stay?'

'Yes,' she said, and realised it was true. 'I don't intend to become your mistress, Jean-Marc. But I won't leave again.'

He watched her in silence for a moment, his dark head resting on the deep red velvet cushions of the couch, and although his face was grim his powerful body was more relaxed, and the whiteness had left his mouth.

'Did you come back for me,' he asked deeply, 'or Dominique? Or both?'

Her face was still with inner tension. 'I came back for you.'

The silence was acute. It was absolute surrender, and they both knew it. She felt as though she had laid her head on the block, her slender neck exposed to his sword.

Suddenly, he sat up, his hands gently moving her aside as he got to his feet. He walked away from her, his black hair ruffled and his hard body weary in the white shirt, black unbuttoned waistcoat, and black trousers.

He went to a painting on the wall, a painting of his mother, and pushed it aside. Behind it was a small grey safe in the wall. His strong hands turned the dial this way, that way, and the safe sprang open.

Jean-Marc withdrew a small deep blue velvet box, and walked back to her. 'This is the Brissac sapphire,' he said tersely, sitting down beside her and opening the box to reveal a vast, perfect blue stone set in antique gold. 'Give me your hand.'

White, dark eyes enormous, she whispered, 'Jean-Marc...'

'Just give me your hand,' he said thickly, and gave a harsh sigh.

Alicia held out her hand, and he took the ring, slid it on to her third finger. She stared down at it, then up at his hard face. 'Are we engaged, Jean-Marc?'

'What else?' he said curtly, and stood up, walked back to the safe, tossed the blue velvet box in it, shut the door, turned the dial and replaced the painting over it.

She watched him, her mouth white. 'You want me to marry you?'

He walked back to her, studying her with hard eyes. 'A little sooner than I expected. But events have moved so quickly. You've always been mine, Alicia—now the rest of the world will know it, too.'

'So romantic, Jean-Marc,' she said with a sudden flare of pain.

'Don't ask me for romance,' he said flatly, walking away from her to the drinks cabinet, unscrewing the whisky bottle. 'I don't have room in my life for that rubbish. I wanted you, I fought for you, I've won you. What more is there to say?'

Alicia almost flinched at the words. But the Brissac ring was heavy on her finger, and she could not deny what he said. He had fought for her and won her. She was deeply in love with him, and although he did not return that love he was making it clear that he would not cheapen her by making her his mistress.

'You could say you love me,' she said with a wry, hurt smile.

'But I won't,' he said curtly, and drained a measure of whisky from his glass, looked at her over one shoulder, his eyes bleak. 'Would you ring for some coffee? I'm going to need it if I stay up all night.'

Alicia picked up the phone, dialled the kitchens, and ordered a pot of strong coffee for two in her husky French accent. Together they drank it, and as time moved on Jean-Marc put his dark head back, studying her through those heavy lids.

'I take it you don't want a showpiece wedding like Dominique?'

Alicia paled at the mention of poor Dominique. 'Jean-Marc, what if something happens to——?'

'Nothing will happen to her,' he said tersely. 'We have to believe that, even if the odds are against it. If these kidnappers are the amateurs I think they are, they won't kill her.' His mouth was grim. 'They may rape her, they may beat her—but they won't actually kill her.'

Alicia closed her eyes, feeling sick.

'Don't think about it.' Jean-Marc touched her shoulder, staring at her. 'Think about our wedding instead.'

Her lids flickered open, stared into his grey eyes. 'No circus, Jean-Marc,' she said huskily, obeying him, pushing the thought of Dominique's possible murder from her appalled mind and catching hold of the wedding instead. 'No Press, no paparazzi, no fashionable guests and no false friends.'

He nodded, mouth firm. 'We'll marry in the Brissac chapel next week. A quiet, dignified ceremony. I'll call Monseigneur Roussillon in the morning.' His grey gaze fell to the crucifix nestling between her breasts, glimmering silver in the shadow of the black dress she wore. 'I want this settled as soon as possible.'

Her eyes traced his hard face. It was the face of a conqueror. 'You've won . . .'

'I know,' he said, and bent his dark head, his mouth closing over hers in a slow, sensual exploration of her mouth, the mouth that now belonged to him and him alone.

Later, when he had kissed her fully, she felt helpless with love, her hair tousled around her flushed face and her dark eyes moving slowly over his tough face as she thought, He doesn't love me, but I love him, and that's all I can ever hope for.

'I must go back to the study now.' Jean-Marc got to his feet with a harsh sigh. 'You go to bed, try and sleep.'

'No,' she said without thinking, standing too. 'I'd never be able to sleep.'

He looked at her with bleak grey eyes and nodded, then opened the door. The police had rung for sandwiches and coffee, and were sitting in exhausted silence, eating and drinking while Pierre ran his hands through his hair and looked inches away from a heart attack.

'Go to bed, Pierre,' Jean-Marc said deeply, putting a hand on his shoulder. 'You're making yourself ill with worry.'

'My poor baby...' Pierre said with a crack in his voice. 'I can't bear to think of what they're doing to her. I won't go to bed—how can I?'

'Be quiet!' Jean-Marc said curtly. 'Don't torture yourself—or me!' He turned to Alicia, his grey eyes appalled, and she instantly went over to him. 'Take him into the drawing-room. Put him on the couch. Get Etienne to bring some blankets.'

Alicia nodded, helped Pierre to stand, and led him into the drawing-room. By the time Etienne had brought the blankets, Pierre was fast asleep. She covered him and tiptoed out.

The night dragged on. Girot spent a lot of time on his walkie-talkie, and the gunfire French became quite comforting as Alicia sat beside Jean-Marc, her hand on his hard thigh, unseen beneath the desk by the others.

The telephone rang at dawn, making them all jump. 'That's it!' Girot took the call. 'They've found her! She's being held at a farmhouse outside St Aubin de Château. Someone saw her run on to the road an hour ago. Two men dragged her back into the farmhouse.' He picked up his jacket, eyes alight. 'Let's go get her!'

Alicia got up, trembling, and Jean-Marc gave her a sharp look. 'You're staying here.'

'You can't make me stay!' she said, shocked. 'What if something happens . . . ?'

'That's exactly why I don't want you there!' Jean-Marc took her face in his hands. 'You must stay here, *chérie*. It could be dangerous if you came.'

'Then why are you going?' she asked hoarsely. 'You could be hurt!'

His mouth hardened into a white line of impatience. 'Just do as I say, Alicia, please!' He kissed her deeply on the mouth, his arms sliding around her, holding her close, and Alicia went with helpless love, her arms around his strong neck, uncaring of the sudden silence as everyone else watched.

When he released her, he stared into her dark eyes and whispered, 'Be here when I get back.' Then he moved away from her, his face hard, picked up his black jacket and was shouldering into it as he left the room.

CHAPTER TEN

IT WAS two hours later that the telephone rang to let Alicia know what had happened. There had been a massive police operation, culminating in a brief shoot-out, followed by Dominique's release. No one had been killed, although two kidnappers were injured and in hospital. They had been a gang of young men, all on drugs. Dominique was in shock, slightly bruised but unhurt, and certainly had not been raped by her captors.

Jean-Marc was unhurt and on his way home in the police limousine. When he stepped out in the cool morning sunlight, Alicia was waiting on the steps to meet him.

'Dominique's in hospital under police guard,' he told her wearily, striding up to her and bending his dark head for a kiss. 'Pierre is with her. He ought to be treated for shock himself. He was in a bad state.'

'How was Dominique?' Alicia followed him as he strode into the hall. 'The police rang, told me she was bruised. How badly...?'

'A black eye,' Jean-Marc said flatly. 'And cuts on her face. She tried to escape twice, apparently.'

'What a brave girl,' Alicia said huskily. 'I don't think I would have had the courage to do that in her position.'

'It was idiotic of her,' he said flatly, then with a harsh sigh, 'But very brave.'

Alicia saw the tired lines around his mouth. 'Do you want some coffee? Something to eat?'

'I just want to go straight to sleep,' he said, running a hand through his black hair.

'Of course,' she said, smiling gently.

'Alicia.' His hand slid to her wrist. 'I don't want to sleep alone.'

Her heart missed a beat.

'I'm too tired to make love to you.' His grey eyes rested on hers. 'I just need to hold you. Will you sleep with me?'

She thought of the ordeal he had just been through, and then her voice said softly, 'Yes, Jean-Marc,' and he stared at her for a second, then gave a cool nod and began to lead her up the stairs. She tried to go into her room as they passed it, saying she had to get her nightdress, but he shook his head, pulling her away, saying,

'I bought you a new one in New York.' They reached his bedroom door, and he opened it. 'I was going to give it to you as a present when I got back. Of course, I didn't get round to it.'

The bedroom was vast, fit for a king, with a carved oak four-poster hung with dark burgundy curtains. The walls were carved oak, too, with the Brissac crest worked into them. The windows were hung with long floor-length heavy curtains.

Jean-Marc strode to the curtains, drew them, shutting out the light. The bedroom was pitch-black until he walked to the bed, bent to flick on the bedside lamp.

Alicia closed the door, her heart thumping. Dry-mouthed, she stared at him, acutely aware that they were finally here, in his bedroom, and that she was about to sleep with him. She believed him when he said he was too tired to make love to her. But nevertheless . . .

'Here.' Jean-Marc took a large white-gold box from his vast oak wardrobe and handed it to her. 'You can put it on in the bathroom. Through there.'

'Thank you,' Alicia said huskily, and moved towards the open bathroom door.

'I'm just going to ring Switzerland,' Jean-Marc told her wearily as she left. 'Cancel that money order. I'll be in bed when you come back, so turn out the light for me, would you?' He slumped down on the bed, picked up the telephone.

Alicia closed the bathroom door. Her heart was fluttering with nerves. She opened the white box, and caught her breath at the beauty of the long scarlet nightdress. Stripping off her clothes, she laid them carefully in the box and closed the lid, then washed and cleaned her teeth before slipping the red silk and lace nightdress on.

Alicia felt so nervous that she hesitated, dry-mouthed and heart palpitating, before she opened the bathroom door and went back into the dimly lit bedroom.

Jean-Marc was fast asleep.

A smile curved her mouth as she tiptoed to the bed and gazed down at him. His mouth was slightly parted as he breathed, his face exhausted, and his broad bare chest and arms were flung out as he lay on his back, wearing nothing but black pyjama trousers.

Alicia tucked him in, slid into bed beside him, and flicked off the light. As she lay close to him, she realised her own deep excitement, and a wry smile curved her mouth as she recognised her dis-appointment, too.

But within minutes she was fast asleep, too.

While they slept, their bodies met and his arms came around her in unconscious possession. Alicia's face was cradled against his warm chest, and he slept with one long leg flung over hers.

It was seven o'clock at night when they both woke up. Jean-Marc woke first, and when he began to kiss her warm white throat she stirred, her eyes flickering open.

He sensed her wakening, and drew his dark head back to look into her eyes. There was a warm, in-timate silence between them, their bodies relaxed and refreshed in the big oak bed, the duvet cradling them as if they were birds in a nest.

'Good morning,' Jean-Marc said deeply, and his grey eyes smiled.

Alicia's hands were warm, splayed on his broad chest. 'What time is it?'

'Nineteen-fifteen!' he said softly. 'My body clock is totally out of sync. How about yours?'

'I lost control of it a long time ago.'

His lashes flickered, he was looking at her full warm mouth, and suddenly the atmosphere tilted as their hearts began to beat in deep thudding unison.

'We're in bed together,' Jean-Marc said under his breath.

Dry-mouthed, she stared at him. 'I know.'

Slowly, taking his time, he lowered his head and when his mouth met hers she opened to him, kissing him back with that slow, unhurried sensuality, feeling the blood begin to move around her body as the sweet, drugging power of love took hold on her.

His hands slid through her hair. Alicia moved her fingers up over his broad, hair-roughened chest, up to his strong throat and into his hair, and the kiss deepened as Jean-Marc's mouth grew more demanding, his eyes closed as tightly as hers, pushing her deeper into the pillows, his arms around her.

It seemed so natural to feel his breathing quicken, to feel those strong hands slide over her bare shoulders, fingering the silky straps of the red nightdress, and when they slid over her full, warm breasts Alicia shivered with a soft moan, arching unconsciously towards him.

The kiss deepened further. His fingers were sliding the bodice aside, baring her breast, and her erect nipples shivered with pulsing excitement as he stroked them, and the hot torture of his kisses made her dizzy with sensation, exchanging love by mouth, her eyes closed and her tongue merging with his, feeling the hard thigh moving slowly, restlessly between hers.

When he started to pull down the red silk nightdress, his heart was thundering as he stroked it to her slender waist, his mouth possessive on hers, and as he stroked it down over her naked hips Alicia started to shake with deep agonising excitement, her whole body trembling in his arms as he slid the nightdress off and found her naked.

'Mon Dieu...!' he whispered hoarsely, sliding his hands over her bare thighs, his heart hammering. 'Je te désire! Chérie... je t'adore...' His mouth closed over hers in a passionate, demanding kiss.

Alicia moaned against his mouth, her breathing hectic and her body flushed with pink colour as arousal spiralled inside her, a tense clutch of agonising tension in the centre of her stomach, her naked thighs brushing against the black pyjama trousers he wore, gasping as she felt the fierce pulsation of his male hardness pressing against her.

'Alicia!' he said raggedly, stroking her breasts. 'I want you! I want to take you...will you fight me, my darling?'

'No...' Alicia looked into his hard, handsome face, her mouth quivering and her inhibitions obliterated by love, knowing that he needed the release lovemaking would bring him, and that she could not deny it to him after the ordeals of the last forty-eight hours. 'No, Jean-Marc...I won't fight you!'

He caught his breath, staring at her. There was a long, tense silence. She could hear his heart beating as he lay against her, and suddenly his mouth hardened. 'Why won't you fight me, Alicia?' he asked under his breath. 'Because my ring is on your finger? Because you feel safe, knowing I will marry you?'

Frowning, she said huskily, 'No...'

'Then why?' His grey eyes were angry. 'I've just asked you to make love with me. But I've asked plenty of times before. What makes this time different?' His mouth went white. 'The Brissac sapphire?'

'No!' She stared up at his hard face. 'You've just been through an ordeal and I——'

'And you are a martyr?' He gave a harsh laugh. 'I think not!'

'Does it matter why I won't fight you?' she asked, hurt and beginning to feel angry.

He looked at her, his eyes furious. 'Yes!' he bit out. 'It matters very much to me!'

'But why?' she demanded, dark eyes flashing. 'I thought it was what you wanted! I thought it was what you needed!'

'It is what I want!' he said harshly. 'And what I need! But Alicia, if I wanted an accommodating wife to submit to marital duties, I could have had my pick of the beauties of Europe!' His eyes flared. 'I want a passionate woman in my bed who wants *me*—not some pretty blue bauble on her finger and the promise of matrimony!'

She caught her breath, fury in her eyes. 'You don't need to explain, Jean-Marc! I can see only too clearly why you suddenly don't feel like taking what I've so foolishly offered!' Her voice rose, shaking with emotion. 'You moved mountains to get me here in your bed, and now that I've finally given in you suddenly feel bored by the whole idea!'

'It's not like that!' he bit out forcefully, grey eyes flashing with rage. 'Don't be such a——'

'Don't add insults to your list of crimes!' Her mouth shook with violent emotion, and she tore the ring from her finger, shouting hoarsely, 'There! There's your Brissac sapphire! Take it and give it to the next girl! I won't hold you to your "promise"!'

'I don't want the damned thing!' He was suddenly very still, staring at her, his heartbeat unsteady. 'Put it back on your finger!'

'No!' she said, hot tears threatening to fall. 'Let me go!'

'Put the ring back on your finger!' he said thickly, dark colour filling his hard face. 'Do you hear me? Put the——'

'It's over, Jean-Marc!' she cried, a tear slipping over her cheek as her mouth trembled betrayingly. 'I was a fool ever to come back here! I knew you'd hurt me! I knew it would end with——'

'I didn't mean to hurt you,' he said under his breath. 'Now put the ring back on your finger and——'

'I can't,' she said bitterly, shaking her head. 'I can't marry you, Jean-Marc! Not feeling like this! I should have known better than to trust my own emotions.' She gave a pained laugh. 'I'd begun to kid myself that you wanted more than sex, more than just another mistress. Now I can see I was fooling myself, and it hurts too much, Jean-Marc, it just——'

'It won't last,' he said grimly, his face white as he held her. 'Now, calm down. Don't walk out just because I behaved like a fool. We'll marry, just as we planned, and you'll forget all about this.'

'No, Jean-Marc,' she whispered, staring at him, her eyes blazing with emotion. 'I won't forget about it. Not for a long, long time—maybe not forever.' She drew a shaky breath. 'I can't turn my feelings off once they're engaged. I know you can, but I can't.'

He tensed, staring at her, his eyes darting over her face. 'Your feelings . . . ?'

'What's the point of lying about it any more?' Alicia said, closing her eyes. 'You've made it clear from the beginning that you would never offer me love. I can't blame you if you stick to that.'

'Love isn't a possibility with me,' he said thickly, flicking his gaze away, his mouth a white line. 'I just can't...'

'I know,' she said with hoarse bitterness. 'But it was always a possibility with me, Jean-Marc! I didn't know it, and maybe neither did you, but it's happened, and I can't turn back the clock!' Her mouth shook as she said, 'I just fell in love with you somewhere along the line, and now I'm——'

'What?' His hands gripped her slim shoulders, grey eyes fierce as he stared down at her. 'Say that again, Alicia!'

She gave a bitter smile. 'I fell in love with you, Jean-Marc,' she said with a choke in her throat. 'I'm in love with you.'

'I fell in love with you the minute I saw your face!' Jean-Marc said unsteadily, staring at her. 'I can't believe we've wasted so much time! When did you realise?'

Stunned, she stared at him, her heart thudding crazily. 'I...' She couldn't speak, her mouth parted and her eyes wide as she stared up into his hard, handsome face.

'I'd given up hope!' Jean-Marc said thickly, and caught her in his arms, holding her close, his hand pushing her face into his strong neck as he stroked her hair.

'Jean-Marc...!' she whispered.

'I can't believe you didn't guess how I felt!' he said under his breath. 'Even when I asked you to marry me, you still believed me when I said I would never love you.' He gave a rough laugh, holding her close. 'It was incredible. I was actually putting the ring on your finger and talking about weddings and you still thought I only wanted your body!'

'You made me believe it!' she whispered, staring at his chest. 'You were so convincing! When you speak in that hard voice I really see the cynical tycoon in you, and he blinds me because I love that part of you as much as this...' Her hand stroked his throat, his dark hair. 'You're as tough as you are passionate.'

'And romantic,' he said with a wry twist of his hard mouth as he drew back to look at her. 'I always knew I'd hear bells ring when I fell in love, and I heard them that first day! I looked at you across the lawns at that stupid garden party, and felt a rush of adrenalin shoot through me like wildfire.'

'You felt it then...?' she asked, incredulous.

Le coup de foudre, chérie!' he said sardonically. 'And I was absolutely knocked for six. I asked who you were, and when they told me you were Alicia Holt, one of the most successful women in Europe, I thought, Yes, she would be, wouldn't she?' His hand stroked her hair as he continued speaking rapidly. 'I saw you go into the house, so as soon as I could I followed you. But you looked at me with such hatred, such rage. I couldn't move. I just stared back at you, thinking, This can't be happening. Doesn't she know how I feel? Then you walked past me, cut me dead, and I wanted to pull the house down around your ears.'

'I had no idea...' she said huskily against his throat.

'I hated you,' he said under his breath, 'but I couldn't stop thinking about you, and when I saw you at the Ritz that day I just went up in flames, watching you walk to the lifts with that man. My woman—and you didn't even notice me watching you. I was so violently angry, I blew a fuse, came to your room and deliberately insulted you.'

Alicia lay against his chest, staring at his skin, overwhelmed by what he was saying, love flooding her, making her heart beat with excitement as she recognised the truths he told.

'But when I saw you...' Jean-Marc went on thickly ' ... so soft and vulnerable and defenceless. No make-up, your hair loose and wet, your eyes staring at me with that obvious sexual fear...'

'I was shaking when you left,' she said huskily, looking up at him through her lashes. 'I remember it vividly. I could barely stand up.'

He laughed under his breath, kissing her mouth. 'My darling, that makes it all worthwhile, because I was shaking too. I wanted so badly to just kiss you until you fell to pieces in my hands, but you looked so vulnerable, and I couldn't bring myself to put you under attack in that state. So I went away and had another little think. But this time I thought about your relationship with David. I saw him in the bar, you see, and I realised how ordinary he was. How completely unlike you. He didn't fit in at the Ritz and he was aware of it. The only person he spoke to was the barman, and then he treated him as a friend. I watched him, and I began to realise what was going on between you. You were so at home there. So obviously accustomed to that lifestyle, and I knew for a fact that you had earned it, not inherited it. So I figured you must have come from a nice, ordinary family. And your powerful rise to prominence had left you straddling two worlds. David represented the old world, didn't he?'

'Yes...' she whispered against his chest, closing her eyes, weak with love.

'And that was why you wanted to marry him,' Jean-Marc said softly, lifting her face to look at him. 'Because he made you feel safe, even though he patently did not love or understand you.'

'He looked on me as someone from another planet,' she said huskily. 'I realised it in the end. But only because of your intervention.'

'Is that how your family treated you?' he asked gently.

'Yes,' she said, eyes tracing his strong face. 'I guess I'm a throwback to another generation, because the rest of my family is and was very different from me.'

He nodded, smiling as he kissed her mouth. 'So was mine. The Brissacs have always been a family of dilettantes, *chérie*. I didn't fit in with that. I always wanted to race about putting rockets under banks and opening new ones all over the world.' He laughed, grey eyes gleaming. 'My father found me rather alarming, and my mother...well, she just used to shrug and say, "I can't think where he gets it from".'

Alicia laughed, pressing her face into his throat. 'My darling, I love you so much! I can't bear to think how nearly I lost you!' Her smile faded and she stared into his hard, handsome face. 'I only came back because of the kidnap. I was worried about Dominique, of course, but I knew you might need me, and——'

'And I would have come after you,' he said with a rueful grin. 'Pride or no pride. I knew you were everything I wanted by then, darling. I would have been tough and uncompromising and I would have cut my throat before telling you how I felt, but I would have got you back.'

Alicia's eyes shone with love. 'You're so determined . . . !'

'Yes,' he said softly, 'and so insanely in love with you.'

'Then,' she asked carefully, 'Isabelle Janvier really is not your mistress any more?'

'Isabelle hasn't been my mistress for months,' he said deeply. 'We split up because she was pushing for marriage, and I knew I couldn't marry her. I didn't love her, Alicia. I like her and see her as a really good friend. But she doesn't understand me. And she wasn't in love with me. She just wanted marriage.'

Alicia nodded. 'She's very beautiful, though. And very successful.'

He smiled. 'In a different way from you and me, Alicia. Isabelle is a possession-oriented woman. She liked the idea of possessing me. But only as her latest acquisition. Only to show off to her friends.'

'To be the woman who caught the Last of the Great French Lovers, you mean?' Alicia studied him soberly, her jealousy of Isabelle dying instantly. 'Yes, that must have become quite a cross for you to bear.'

He made a wry face. 'I was nicknamed that when I was very young. It stuck. By the time I was old enough to realise quite what a nuisance it was—it was too late.' He gave a cool laugh, shrugging broad shoulders. 'I'll be the Last of the Great French Lovers till the day I die. There's nothing I can do about it.'

'Well,' she said softly, looking at him through her lashes, 'I must admit, you certainly live up to it!'

He looked down at her with a smile. 'Do I, *chérie*?' he said under his breath, and lowered his dark head as her heart began to thud faster. His hard mouth closed over hers in a kiss that made her heart burn with slow excitement and the power of love.

She was breathless when he drew away, her eyes blazing. 'Jean-Marc . . .'

'I've waited so long to hear you say my name like that!' he whispered, staring into her face. 'You make my life so complete, Alicia.'

'I love you,' she said with feeling.

He kissed her again, said thickly, 'Think of what we can do together. How exciting our lives will be when they're joined, and how richly fulfilling. I love everything about you. I can't wait to know you utterly, to hear you talk every night, tell me what you've done, what you plan to do.' He smiled. 'We'll be able to tell each other how busy and exciting life is . . . and make love, hold hands, grow old together.'

'You still want me to design Dominique's wedding?' she asked huskily.

'Of course!' he said, dark brows lifting. 'I want you to keep working, for as long as you want to.'

'I'd be bored silly if I stopped working,' she admitted, smiling. 'I love to feel all those cylinders going!'

His smile understood and loved her. 'But you must stop,' he said, 'when you get pregnant.'

A quiver of violent emotion ran over her face and she felt Jean-Marc slide his strong hands possessively down to her belly, making her say in a hoarse whisper, 'Oh, God, children...' her eyes blazed with love '...your children!'

'Our children!' he said, his eyes intense. 'And just think of what they'll be like, *chérie*!'

Her face sobered. 'They might not be like either of us, darling. They might just be themselves.'

He studied her, grey eyes lit with love. 'You're right,' he said deeply. 'We must never make any of them feel they don't belong. But maybe one of them will be like us, Alicia. Maybe a son. Maybe he'll become President of France or——'

'How many children are you planning to have?' she asked, laughing.

'As many as you want to give me,' he said huskily, and kissed her.

Her eyes moved over his strong face. 'I'd give you the moon and stars for your birthday, Jean-Marc. You changed my life completely. You made me real again. You made me capable of love and of trust.' Her voice shook with the realisation of how much he had given her. 'If you asked me for a hundred children, I'd give them, because nothing could ever repay the debt I owe you.'

'Alicia,' he said, 'I love you. There is no debt. There's only the future. And personally,' his gaze dropped to her full red mouth, 'I can't wait to rush into it.'

His mouth closed over hers, and she twined her arms around his strong neck, filled with love, her naked skin next to his, their bodies beginning the slow blend until they were one person, and she knew this was what she had waited her whole life for: her other half.

Next Month's Romances

Each month you can choose from a world of variety in romance
with Mills & Boon. Below are the new titles to look out for next
month, why not ask either Mills & Boon Reader Service or your
Newsagent to reserve you a copy of the titles you want to buy —
just tick the titles you would like to order and either post to Reader
Service or take it to any Newsagent and ask them to order your
books.

Please save me the following titles:	Please tick	√
PAST LOVING	**Penny Jordan**	
WINTER OF DREAMS	**Susan Napier**	
KNIGHT TO THE RESCUE	**Miranda Lee**	
OUT OF NOWHERE	**Patricia Wilson**	
SECOND CHANCE FOR LOVE	**Susanne McCarthy**	
MORE THAN A DREAM	**Emma Richmond**	
REVENGE	**Natalie Fox**	
YESTERDAY AND FOREVER	**Sandra Marton**	
NO GENTLEMAN	**Kate Walker**	
CATALINA'S LOVER	**Vanessa Grant**	
OLD LOVE, NEW LOVE	**Jennifer Taylor**	
A FRENCH ENCOUNTER	**Cathy Williams**	
THE TRESPASSER	**Jane Donnelly**	
A TEMPTING SHORE	**Dana James**	
A LOVE TO LAST	**Samantha Day**	
A PLACE OF WILD HONEY	**Ann Charlton**	

If you would like to order these books from Mills & Boon Reader
Service please send £1.70 per title to: Mills & Boon Reader
Service, P.O. Box 236, Croydon, Surrey, CR9 3RU and quote your
Subscriber No:..(If applicable)
and complete the name and address details below. Alternatively,
these books are available from many local Newsagents including
W.H.Smith, J.Menzies, Martins and other paperback stockists
from 14th August 1992.

Name:...

Address:...

....Post Code:........................

**To Retailer: If you would like to stock M&B books please
contact your regular book/magazine wholesaler for details.**

You may be mailed with offers from other reputable companies as a result of this application.
If you would rather not take advantage of these opportunities please tick box ☐